TURNING THE TABLES ON BURNOUT

Break free, burn brighter!

ANN M DIMENT

For more information, email anndimentartist@gmail.com.

ISBN: 979-8-88759-731-7 - paperback

ISBN: 979-8-88759-732-4 - ebook

GET YOUR FREE GIFT!

To get the best experience with this book, I've found readers who download and use the resources from the website below are able to more quickly take the next steps needed to break free from the burnout cycle for good and live a more joyful and resilient life.

You can download meditations,
worksheets and more resources at:
https://worksafeandwell.co.uk/turning-the-tables-on-burnout-book/

DEDICATION

*This book is dedicated to all who struggle
to find the energy to get through the day.*

You are enough.

You are loved.

You can find another way.

TABLE OF CONTENTS

Introduction

Have you ever experienced burnout?

How did it feel?

Would you want to go through it again?

This book is written to share what I have learned on my own journey of breaking free from over 20 years suffering repeated depressive episodes and trapped in the burnout cycle, due to overworking and perfectionism. By 'burnout' I mean the state of complete and utter mental and physical exhaustion that rips your life apart and renders you unable to function as your body and mind shut down to protect you. I'll give a more 'official' definition later in the book, and as we are all individuals, you may experience it in different ways to anyone else. The important thing is to recognise how that 'shutdown' shows up for you, then to listen to your body and trust that there is a way out of this, and you *can* recover.

After struggling with self-criticism and shame about my poor mental health throughout my twenties and thirties, I was diagnosed with complex PTSD when I was 38 , and finally realised that it was not my weakness and inability to cope with work and life that was causing me to stay stuck in this destructive cycle of burnout and breakdowns. This led me to take a new path to healing and recovery as I pieced together the experiences, beliefs, and behaviours that were imprinted in me by society, my family, and our working culture that were draining me and had shaped my mind to keep me in a loop of always trying to keep myself 'safe' from conflict or criticism.

Once I decided to take action to break free of the burnout cycle, I began a 12-year journey of discovery and healing, and found a path through to a more joyful and less-stressed life.

I now use my own experiences of recovering from burnout to help my coaching clients and social media followers to build their own resilience toolkits. I also host the Creating Resilience podcast, where I talk to inspirational guests and share their stories about beating their own burnout.

In this book you will find simple and effective tools that I have learned over this journey that you can use to beat burnout. Also included in each chapter are lots of ' burn brighter' prompts for you to take small steps towards building your own resilience toolkit and to start turning the tables on how you respond to life's challenges.

This book is designed to empower you to question old beliefs about how you work and spend your time and energy so you can protect your boundaries and break free from burnout too. It will show you how to recognise the symptoms of burnout and reach out for support without feeling shame or guilt. My mission is to create a world of work and education which is trauma-informed and does not damage anyone's health or wellbeing, where we are all treated as individuals, with dignity and respect, and compassion and empathy are embedded in everything we do. Whatever you have survived or are going through right now, you have got this you are already enough and are not 'broken'. With enough time, the right tools, and a solid support network, it is possible for you to create recovery, so you can burn brighter and break free from burnout for good.

What this book is NOT.

If you are anything like me, please don't use this book as another 'should' added onto your to-do list. This book is not meant to be a source of stress; rather, it is more of an invitation to learn, grow, and turn the tables on beliefs that have been harming you for too long.

Together, we can gently transform those beliefs into new ways of living and working that are sustainable and centred around your own unique abilities, experiences, and needs so you can start living and not just existing every day.

What to expect from reading this book.

By the end of this book, if you implement the resilience tools shared here, it is entirely possible for you to be living a well-balanced life, where work is just one part of your identity, and not something that defines you or causes you psychological harm.

> *"The key is not to prioritize what's on your schedule, but to schedule your priorities."*
> —Stephen Covey, Author

Chapter 1

Stop the World,
I want to get off!

*"Never get so busy making a living that you
forget to make a life."*

—Dolly Parton, Country Singer

Have you ever had the experience of lying in bed, or being in the shower, when your body and mind just stop functioning? I mean when you really feel frozen, as if someone flipped a switch in your head to say,

'That's it!

I'm done.

I can't face the world today.'

Or maybe you have had days (or weeks) when you wished you had a magic remote control with a big shiny 'pause' button. Maybe you just need a moment to breathe and escape the never-ending list of stuff you think you *should* be doing.

Those moments were the story of my twenties and thirties. When the panic, overwhelm and breakdowns happened in response to the triggers that may have seemed perfectly normal to others but caused me to tip into survival mode, it was terrifying, depressing, and at times, pretty miserable and lonely. I would never wish those feelings of utter despair, exhaustion, isolation, self-loathing, and fear on any other human.

I have spent most of my adult life not only trying to understand why it was happening to me and how to prevent it happening again, and in doing so, I learned that many of these were symptoms of burnout. I have since turned my focus toward educating, campaigning, and coaching others on what burnout is and how to break free from its grip.

It is a sad reality that if you burnout once, unless you recognise why and how you got to that state, and make some changes in how you value your own time and energy, it is very likely that it will continue to happen. Western society's working practices are based on the idea that working hard makes you successful. Due to this, it all seems to be set up to demand faster, more productive, 'always on' levels of effort from us.

Unless we have our own inbuilt strategies to form and hold strong boundaries to protect our time and energy, many of us become trapped in a destructive burnout cycle that gradually erodes away our health and mental well-being with each turn of the burnout wheel.

The first part of this book (chapters 1-6) will take you on an exploration journey to understand what burnout is and what really causes it, as well as how your mind and body can be harmed by it.

In the second part of the book (chapters 7-11) I'll show you how you can recover from burnout and become resistant to it, by using tools you can add to your resilience toolkit.

To get the most out of this book, try the *burn brighter step* action points and reflection questions at the end of each chapter. I've also created a downloadable worksheet to save you writing on your book as you might like to pass it on after you're done with it. See the book website listed in the 'further resources' section at the end.

You might also want to start a journal to document your own recovery journey and record your progress and insights as you work through the book. It could be a form of therapy in itself if you get creative and use the journal for adding colour or pictures (wait – that's all going to be described in chapter 10 so let's not skip ahead!)

So, I'm not mad?

My story is a classic one. Having many traumatic experiences in my childhood and teen years, I did not realise until adulthood how much they had shaped my brain to be a prime candidate for burning out.

It started when I was just five years old, and had not long started primary school. My mother came to pick me up from school one day and instead of walking home (we lived in the same street as the school), we took a bus across town to visit my grandmother. As a five-year-old, I didn't suspect anything and really enjoyed an unexpected sleepover at my grandparents' house. The next day however, instead of returning home to my father, we got on a train and left for what I was told was a 'holiday', but turned out to be a completely new life, as my mum was in fact running away to live with the man she had been having an affair with and I didn't get to see my father until nearly two years later, when the custody battle began.

This was the start of many years of trauma that shaped my young brain, and during the first few years as my dad eventually found out where I had been taken to and started legal proceedings to try and regain custody, I was subjected to a whole range of parental alienation behaviours from my mom and step family to try to turn me against my dad. I was conditioned into permanent survival mode and later, in my teens, after both parents had remarried and new siblings appeared in my new families, my mom developed alcohol dependency and mental ill health that resulted in physical and emotional abuse when she wasn't coping or just wanted to take out their frustrations on someone. The impact of these experiences (and more that I'll share later in the book) showed up in my adult life as hypervigilance, constant people pleasing, and apologising for pretty much everything, regardless of whether it was my fault or not, so it's not really surprising that I had less emotional resilience to deal with stress and bullying at work.

To get through my teenage years, I buried myself in my studies and joined pretty much every lunchtime and after-school club that I could, so I spent less time at home and kept my anxious mind busy. As I reached the end of my schooling I realised that I could escape by getting away to University, even though nobody in my family had ever done that before. This was met with disapproval, as in my step-family's view, it was a waste of time for girls to get a college education as they only end up getting married and having children!

I stuck it out and got to university, and spent the next seven years successfully completing a Bachelor's then a Master's degree and the impact of my experiences growing up didn't really start taking effect until I escaped the family unit and started to process everything whilst living independently.

It is no surprise then that I had various periods of mental illness during my 20s and was diagnosed with depression. Navigating the mental-health challenges early in my career and whilst starting my family was really tough.

The health & safety career I ended up following was, I have recently realised, because I wanted to keep people safe. Because of the experiences in my younger years, I felt so passionate about keeping people safe that if people didn't do what they were supposed to be doing to protect themselves and others from harm I'd get really stressed, and that, of course, made me more vulnerable to burnout!

But that's enough about me for now; let's move on to understand how your brain works so you can understand what burnout is and how it happens.

Burn-Brighter Step:

Let's start with creating a timeline to understand when you have burnt out.

Draw a line across the middle of a sheet of paper and mark divisions for every decade of your life. Above the line, mark each time you have burned out (the year is enough detail). Below the line, mark life events and incidents that might have contributed to your exhaustion.

You could also note the reasons in your worksheet or journal. Think about all the possible factors that could have contributed.

Don't skip these reflections! It would really enhance your journey through this book if you take a few moments to think about the stories you have been telling yourself about why you burn out.

Chapter 2
Your Amazing Brain!

*"...the brain is the most miraculous mass of protoplasm
on this earth and perhaps in our galaxy.
Its potential is virtually unknown."*
—Marian Diamond (Marian)

Your brain is amazing!

The Human brain is a 'supercomputer,' coordinating millions of sensory, electrical and chemical processes simultaneously and generating around 60,000 thoughts every day. Even though it is only approximately 2 percent of the total mass of your body – it uses up around 20 percent of your energy, so it is important to make sure that you have enough energy to support healthy brain function and you most definitely don't want to waste that precious energy worrying about the small stuff or responding to stressors that are burning you out.

It used to be thought that once we reached adulthood our brains were 'fixed' and then continuously deteriorated as we got older. But in 1964, eminent neuroscientist Marian Diamond (no relation!) made a discovery that completely turned the world of brain science on its head (pun intended!).

This ground-breaking study demonstrated for the first time that the brain could rewire and make new connections and quite literally rebuild itself, well after childhood. Adult rats in an under-stimulated environment developed much smaller brains than those with an enriched and simulated environment, proving that the phrase 'use it or lose it' applies to our minds as well as our bodies (Diamond et al. #). This means that the more we learn and stimulate our minds and create bonds with our support circle and society, the bigger and better our brains will get. Any athlete will know that the more you train, the more muscle you gain – well, the same applies to our brains.

Diamond's team later showed in 1985 that to thrive and grow our brain mass we need five key factors:

1. Diet (you are what you eat!)
2. Exercise (not a popular suggestion but it is scientific fact)
3. Challenge
4. Newness
5. Love/connection

But how does this apply to burnout?

Well, if our minds are healthy, then we should be more resilient to dealing with the chronic stressors that cause us to burn out, but what Diamond's study demonstrated here was that the environment in which we live and how we use our brains has a significant impact on brain development. So as we are spending more than a third of our time at work (in a typical eight-hour day), if we are not mentally challenged by the work tasks, or are doing boring repetitive work, or don't have good working relationships or work in isolation, this can affect our brains both physically and mentally.

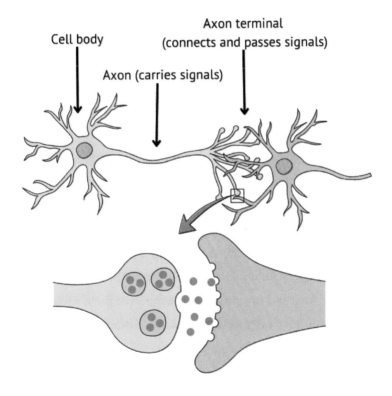

Where nerve cells connect, they pass chemical signals (neurotransmitters) across the space between them (synapse).

Stress in the Brain

Chronic stress has been reported to produce an excess of signalling molecules called glucocorticoids, which have been shown to be toxic to the neurons that our brain is made from, so when we use the term 'toxic stress' it is because the stress response is quite literally poisoning our brains (Meaney et al.).

Let's look at how the brain works to see how the stress response is triggered and how it affects the different brain functions. In the classic medical diagrams, the brain is divided up into many different regions. It was once thought these regions acted separately, but recent advances in neuroscience have shown that they are interconnected and act as complex networks. These networks communicate with each other and regulate all the thousands of functions your brain does every second of every day you are alive, whether it's the basic life support stuff like making sure your heart beats and you are breathing, or the sensory processing of your surroundings so you can make sense of the environment you are in and respond in real time to things you see, hear, smell, feel and taste, as well as generating and responding to your endless stream of thoughts.

Let's look in a bit more detail at some of these networks so you can understand how they work and address the workplace stressors that lead to burnout:

1. The Emotion-regulation network
2. The Attention networks.
3. The Selfing and control networks
4. The Empathy networks.

The Emotion-regulation network

As an Emotional Freedom Techniques (EFT) practitioner, I often see clients who are not aware of, or cannot face admitting their emotions they are feeling, as they are scared, ashamed or unable to connect with them after years of conditioning. Being truly able to identify, and accept how you are feeling is a key tool in your resilience toolkit, so let's understand a bit more about how this network works in your brain.

The hippocampus, which is situated in the limbic system, is involved in expressing emotions. It has been shown in people who are depressed, or who have PTSD, that this part of the brain gets coated in calcium deposits from the elevated levels of the stress hormone, cortisol. All this cortisol can cause the hippocampus to actually shrink, reducing the capacity to express or feel emotions.

A key player in regulating emotions is the Thalamus – which acts as a receiver of sensory signals and transmitter from the spinal cord to the prefrontal cortex (PFC) region of the brain. One region of the PFC has a hotline to your stress response button – the amygdala, which is a structure the size of a peanut that tells your brain when to trigger the stress response, and to put understand more how this works, here is a poem I wrote about it:

I am the Amygdala, I run your stress response

With a hotline to your senses,

all tucked up in your bonce.

When danger is approaching, it's me who gets the shout.

Then I spring into action, sending signals to get out!
I'm constantly on duty, with your eyes and ears and skin,
Though no bigger than a peanut, I rule you like a king!

So in highly stressed or depressed brains, where parts like the hippocampus have been shown to shrink, the Amygdala grows to compensate. As it is being constantly stimulated, it creates new neural connections, following the Hebb's Law rule of "nerves that fire together, wire together". (Hebb #). This discovery showed that when an electrical signal is passed through two neurons for a short period of time they form new connections, so the more you activate parts of your brain by repeating thoughts and responses, the stronger and larger those network connections become, in other words, you can rewire your brain just by thinking!

A larger amygdala and smaller hippocampus would mean that you are more likely to produce a stress response and feel less connected with your emotions, often described as a 'numbing' feeling that is so familiar when we are withdrawing from the world to protect ourselves. Conversely, if we find ways to tune down our stress response (you'll discover some later in this book) and shrink the amygdala, then reduce the amount of cortisol pulsing through our system and protect the hippocampus from these deposits so we can tune in more to our emotions and grow this part of the brain. It sounds simple, but it needs focus and practice using the tools I will describe later in this book.

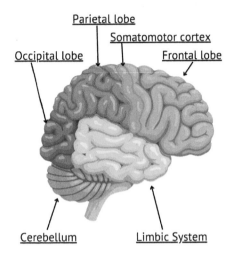

Parietal lobe

Somatomotor cortex

Occipital lobe

Frontal lobe

Cerebellum

Limbic System

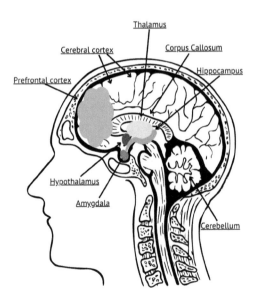

Thalamus

Cerebral cortex

Corpus Callosum

Hippocampus

Prefrontal cortex

Hypothalamus

Amygdala

Cerebellum

The Attention network.

Have you noticed that when you are calm, you are able to get more done and focus better?

As we learned from the previous section, once the amygdala is firing, it begins instructing your brain to fire out a cocktail of stress chemicals. It does this to prime your anxious and stressed brain to be hypervigilant, ready to fend off whatever is threatening you. The executive functions of the 'thinking' brain get stopped or drowned out by the more urgent need to stay safe from whatever perceived threat your brain has decided you are under.

In contrast, when we are calm, the Attention Network is able to take over. This network of brain regions includes the prefrontal cortex (PFC), corpus callosum and somatomotor regions, which process pain, touch and our sense of presence in our environment. When we are truly focussed, we feel grounded and connected with our body and senses, which in turn helps us better focus, in a repeating, reinforcing cycle.

We will learn in Chapter 3 that one of the defining traits of burnout is *increased mental distance from one's job, or feelings of negativism or cynicism related to one's job,* so when you are in a state of, or approaching burnout, the attention networks of your brain will not be as active, so if you find yourself having difficulty focussing on your work it may be useful to consider if burnout is the cause.

The good news is that researchers have shown that the attention network , like any other part of the brain, can be developed and strengthened by tools such as meditation in just a few days. A randomised controlled study by Tang et al (Tang et al.) demonstrated changes in self-regulation networks in students after only five days of meditation practice, and they replicated the results in younger and older subjects in later trials. They showed using neuroimaging techniques that meditation improved activation and connectivity in the attention network areas of the brain. We'll learn more about tools like this in Chapter 9.

The 'Selfing' and control networks

Our brains are wired for self-preservation, and part of this is noticing the negatives in life. We are more likely to notice negatives, as doing so keeps us from danger. The key player in this is the default mode network.

This part of the brain was found by researchers at Washington University to be more active when the brain was in a resting state, (Raichle) and deactivated when the brain was engaged in attention demanding tasks.

Its discovery was an unexpected consequence of brain-imaging studies in which various tasks that were new, attention-demanding, and non-self-referring were compared with resting either with eyes closed or with fixing focus on a specific spot. What the researchers observed was that the default mode network activity decreased whilst doing these active tasks when compared with during the relaxed states. This emphasised the significance of the brain's internal activity even when resting. The brain as an organ uses up to 20 percent of your energy even when you are resting or meditating, so that energy is diverted to this network in those states.

These selfing and control networks have been further studied by teams looking to understand what part they play in our brain health and disease. One part of the network has been found to be a key player in communicating information sensed from our external world to the hypothalamus, the amygdala (that pesky peanut-sized stress response trigger), and the midbrain. So this network influences our social behaviour, mood control, and motivational drive, all of which are important components of our personality. (Öngür and Price)

When we are burned out we typically spend less time in the resting state, '*be*ing' mode, and more in '*do*ing' mode as we work harder and longer. As we have learned already in this book, if you don't use it you lose it, so a simple way of boosting the selfing and control networks is to spend more time resting – yes, it really is that simple, do nothing, so you can divert that brain's energy to those all-important control networks! There is a growing movement of 'radical rest' groups that encourage taking more time to do nothing and just 'be' every day, and by understanding why this is important to our brain health, perhaps it might not be a bad thing to try?

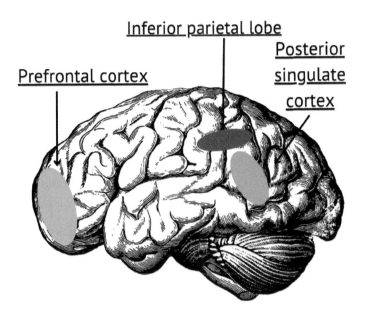

Inferior parietal lobe

Posterior
singulate
cortex

Prefrontal cortex

The Default mode network (DMN) is a network
of interacting brain regions that remains active
when you are not focused on the outside world

The Empathy network.

The term "empathy" is used to describe a wide range of experiences. Emotion researchers generally define empathy as *the ability to sense other people's emotions, coupled with the ability to imagine what someone else might be thinking or feeling.* ("Empathy Definition & Meaning"), and it is defined in the Merriam Webster dictionary as:

'the action of understanding, being aware of, being sensitive to, and vicariously experiencing the feelings, thoughts, and

31

experience of another of either the past or present without having the feelings, thoughts, and experience fully communicated in an objectively explicit manner
also: the capacity for this' ("Empathy Definition & Meaning")

These parts of the brain are associated with compassion and connecting with the rest of our community and our families. It also includes brain structures that connect with physical signals in the body such as pain, and is linked with emotional intelligence.

The term 'emotional intelligence' was created by Peter Salavoy and John Mayer in their article "Emotional Intelligence" in 1990 (Salovey, and Mayer). It was later popularised by psychologist Daniel Goleman in his 1995 book *Emotional Intelligence* (Goleman) and can be is described as the ability to:

- *Recognize, understand and manage our own emotions and;*
- *Recognize, understand and influence the emotions of others.*

In 'Emotional Intelligence' (Goleman), Goleman explains that although it is largely shaped by early experiences, emotional intelligence can be nurtured and strengthened throughout our adult life. This can have great benefits to our health, our relationships, and our work, and of course – protect us from burnout!

The empathy network is only really activated once the other three networks described earlier in this chapter are developed. It is the top level network in the brain which lights up when we see people suffering, or when we need to take care of children, friends, or members of our community.

Psychologists Daniel Goleman and Paul Ekman (Goleman and Wheeland) have identified three components of empathy: **Cognitive, Emotional, and Compassionate**

- Cognitive empathy: Is understanding how others see things, what mental models they use and how to understand others. It is an essential skill for interacting with the world and the people we work and live with.
- Emotional empathy is a more social skill about establishing rapport and being able to sense what someone else is feeling.
- Compassionate empathy, from a place of love and wanting to care for someone. This is in the emotional area of the brain and opens us up to a more vulnerable state as we are offering stronger emotional connections with the person.

Empathy can cause people to feel pain in the same way they see or experience other people feeling pain. If people are describing a painful experience, that can lead to our empathy networks lighting up. The Empathy network is also connected with happiness and joy circuits, and these can be strengthened with greater practice of empathy, so we can learn to imagine what it's like to be in somebody else's shoes and understand the emotions they are feeling.

While empathy can be a good thing, it can also be a big part of burnout. If we are constantly showing empathy for other people's suffering, especially if we don't allow ourselves to think about how we're feeling, we can easily become overwhelmed and exhausted.

If we are stressed and lose sight of our own needs as we are empathising with everyone but ourselves—that can negatively affect our mental health. In contrast, when we're calm, we can focus our attention, and empathy, in a way that actually is good for us and those around us. We feel rewarded when we've helped other people, when we have done good things for other people. Our empathy networks can help us activate some rewards like dopamine and other 'happy hormones' when we do things that help other people.

So, what can we conclude about your amazing brain? Well, in Chapter 6, we will learn that early developmental trauma can affect how the brain develops and make survivors more vulnerable to a whole range of physical- and mental-health challenges in later life, but we have learned in this chapter that the brain is a miraculous shape-shifting mass that can adapt and regrow if given the right conditions to thrive and stay healthy.

These basic factors include.

- A healthy Diet - containing all the right fatty acids and nutrients to form new neurons and not clog the brain's blood supply (you are what you eat!)
- Exercise - to keep the body healthy and keep a sufficient oxygen and blood supply flowing to the brain (not always a popular suggestion but it is scientific fact!)
- Challenge - to enable us to strengthen and grow existing neural networks.
- Newness - to stay curious, feel accomplishment when you learn new skills and grow neural networks.
- Love/connection - to meet our basic human safety needs of being part of a 'tribe.' We will learn more about this in chapter 8.

Burn-Brighter Step:

1. Let's put all the learning in this chapter into a work context- and see if your work is good for your brain health:

- Do your work tasks stimulate you?
- Are you challenged mentally by your work and have opportunities to learn new skills or information?
- Do you feel connected and valued by your work?
- Does your job/lifestyle allow you to be active?
- Does your job/lifestyle enable you to maintain a healthy diet?

If you have been unable to tick one of these boxes, then you may be more susceptible to burning out and might want to look at ways of making some changes to how you work and plan your days to enable you to stay in balance and be kind to your mind. You will find lots of tools in Chapter 9 of this book to help you build resilience and better balance in your life so you can burn brighter and stay at the top of your game.

2. Here's a bonus step to try next time you are feeling overwhelmed or stressed:

- Take a few deep breaths (to slow down the amygdala response and get some oxygen to your brain)
- Notice five things you can see around you (to connect with your environment and tune into your selfing network)
- Now notice four things you can hear (this takes attention away from the racing thoughts and distracts that pesky amygdala)
- Notice three things you can touch (This connects you back into your body and to your attention network)
- Now notice two things you can smell (This encourages you to breathe through your nose and tune into a sense you often don't pay much attention to)
- And finally one thing you can taste (This can remind you of the last thing you ate or drank, or perhaps your toothpaste if you have just brushed your teeth)

This simple exercise to connect you back to your senses pulls you out of the emotional response and back into your attention network. In other words, it takes you out of your head and back into your body. Stopping the amygdala-inspired fire alarm allows space for you to get some perspective on whatever has triggered the chain reaction before you get trapped into the full fight/flight/freeze/fawn cycle.

Chapter 3

What is Burnout?

*"We need to do a better job of putting ourselves
higher on our own 'to do' list."*
Michelle Obama, former US First Lady

In Chapter 1, I shared some of my story of burning out and
how my mental health and PTSD contributed to my getting stuck in a cycle of burnout after burnout. But is burnout
really about us as individuals not being able to cope?

This book is called *Turning the Tables on Burnout* so let's
explore what that means.

Think about your beliefs as a tabletop; solid, sturdy, and
stable. We often don't think of them in this way, but they are
just thoughts, formed from the understanding and experiences
that may be your own, or are passed on by your family, friends,
and social circles. These experiences and understandings make
up the 'legs' of your table.

One of these legs in the belief about burnout may be that
it is your fault, because society, employers, and the media have

built a convenient smokescreen around work and productivity, and the much misused and misunderstood term 'resilience' to imply that people who burnout are unable to cope or are not good at managing their schedules.

In this book, we will work through some of these commonly held beliefs about burnout and help to smash some of them and the stigma they provoke. That leg that claims burnout is an individual 'weakness' or failure needs to be knocked out from under your table right now!

In this chapter, we'll start with really understanding what burnout is so you can think about why and how it happens.

Burnout Definition

It is widely known that our working populations are getting more stressed and are more commonly burning out. A 2020 survey of UK employees by a global employee benefits and rewards organisation, Perkbox, claimed that a staggering 79 percent of British adults in employment reported experiencing work-related stress, (an increase of 20 percent since 2018), and this has been echoed in many other countries across the globe.

This 'burnout spike' in 2020 is not surprising, as our 'normal' way of working and living was so dramatically changed by the COVID-19 pandemic. Individuals had to cope with a whole-sea change in how we live and work including; juggling working from home, increased workloads, home schooling, job insecurity, business and financial worries, on top of health concerns, loss of social structures, and being unable to plan anything!

"Burnout" as a term was coined in the 1970s by the American psychologist Herbert Freudenberger. He used it to describe the consequences of severe stress and job expectations in medical practitioners and other "helping" professions, where doctors and nurses would often feel exhausted, listless, and unable to cope with the demands of their jobs. Now, it is recognised that burnout can affect anyone who is exposed to chronic stress at work.

It took nearly fifty years, but burnout was officially recognised by the World Health Organisation (WHO) in 2019 as a **work-related** health issue, not something that is due to any individual 'weakness' or mental-health issues. The pandemic brought burnout into many of our lives to a greater degree and has focused minds on how we start creating a path out of what is being recognised as a global burnout epidemic.

In researching this book and writing my blog posts on the Work Safe and Well website (worksafeandwell.co.uk/) since 2018 , the same pattern emerges in the stories published:

- Individuals were made ill by workplace stress.
- They took time out to recover.
- They came back to either more stress, or no changes to the stressors that made them ill in the first place.
- And the cycle repeats.......
Sound familiar?

I sometimes want to shout it from the rooftops: A short break from work doesn't cut it! Neither do free yoga classes, fruit on Fridays or subsidised bike travel if your workload is still the same and you have to deal with a whole heap of other work-related stresses that are still there when you've eaten the free banana and unknotted yourself on the yoga mat.

We need to drop the stigma around burnout, stop looking at it like an individual problem, and start tackling the causes. If we can do that, then the millions of people suffering from this entirely preventable and *life-changing* condition can stop feeling guilt and shame about finding the support they need to recover.

Remember, this is categorised by the World Health Organisation ("Burn-out an "occupational phenomenon": International Classification of Diseases") as a workplace phenomenon, not a medical condition, and it shows up like this:

> *"Burn-out is a syndrome conceptualized as resulting from chronic workplace stress that has not been successfully managed. It is characterized by three dimensions:*
> - *feelings of energy depletion or exhaustion.*
> - *increased mental distance from one's job, or feelings of negativism or cynicism related to one's job; and*
> - *reduced professional efficacy."* ("Burn-out an "occupational phenomenon": International Classification of Diseases")

So, when we read headlines like this:

'A career change saved my life': the people who built better lives after burnout' (Saner)

We need to recognise that the chronic ***workplace stress*** in the organisations they are leaving behind is being allowed to continue and not being addressed. The individual may have found a solution, but the environment that caused the problem lives on. People are choosing to leave their jobs, or take significant pay cuts just to escape or reduce the harm that their work is causing them. This is not a real solution, but it's the best option many people have. Here's a bit more about my experience.

I mentioned previously that I didn't manage to see a psychologist and get a diagnosis of complex post-traumatic stress disorder (cPTSD) until I was 38 and had already started a family of my own. The key symptoms of cPTSD are perfectionism and avoiding criticism or conflict. In some ways it helped me do a better job, but that came at my own expense. It can lead to burnout because working hard to overachieve means you never feel good enough. You don't recognise everything you have done, only noticing the things you haven't done or that didn't go well.

It got so bad that in 2012 that I was off work for nearly nine months with anxiety, depression, and complete exhaustion to the point that I couldn't even walk my kids to school or look after them properly at home (adding to my feelings of inadequacy as I strived to be a better mother than the one I had experienced). In the preceding year, my grandmother and stepfather had died a few months apart, opening up a whole can of emotional worms to deal with on top of the cPTSD diagnosis I had just received. I was working in a high-pressure and often hostile environment as a health and safety manager in a university research school. My manager at the time had started to bully me because I was exposing some poor working practices and challenging how they were running things. This additional pressure, intimidation and harassment on top of the grief and coming to terms with the cPTSD diagnosis unsurprisingly tipped me into burnout.

After nine months off work (whilst still dealing with harassment from my manager), I finally managed to get well enough to return to work, but nothing had changed in my working arrangements, in fact they had deteriorated as the manager ramped up the pressure as we negotiated a phased return. The only solution that Occupational health could advise me to do was to cut my working hours to reduce my exposure to the manager, but this also meant taking a 20-percent pay cut, (which in turn affected my final salary pension and long-term financial security). As I had to carry on doing the same job in reduced hours, the stress got even worse as I not only resented the fact that I felt like I was being penalised financially for being ill, and the issues with the manager had not been resolved. So, the spiralling cycle of stress continued, and you don't need too much imagination to see how that affected my recovery, do you?

Burn-Brighter Step:

Think about your tabletop now, relating to your reflections from Chapter 1.

- Can you think of any different reasons why you have burned out? Maybe some reasons that are less focussed on personal failures and more on the system you were trapped in?
- What organisations do you know about that are taking burnout seriously?
- How would your employer respond if you told them you were feeling burned out?

Chapter 4

What are the costs of burning out?

"Imagine life as a game in which you are juggling some five balls in the air. You name them – work, family, health, friends and spirit and you're keeping all of these in the air. You will soon understand that work is a rubber ball. If you drop it, it will bounce back. But the other four balls are made of glass. If you drop one of these, they will be irrevocably scuffed, marked, nicked, damaged, or even shattered.
They will never be the same. You must understand that and strive for balance in your life."

—Brian Dyson, former Vice Chairman
and COO of Coca-Cola

Now that we have a better understanding about what the real causes of burnout are, let's take a look at what impact burnout might have.

When we talk about the costs of burning out, it is not just the immediate productivity costs of taking time off work or the short and long-term financial costs of cutting hours like I shared in the last chapter. What would it cost you, personally, if you couldn't work for a week, six months, a year, or not even be able to go back to your job again? What might it cost your organisation?

What would it cost you if you couldn't work anymore because you were so burnt out you could not function? Maybe:

- Your Job?
- Your Health?
- Your Family Life?
- Your Home?

Do you have enough (or any) savings or a backup plan if you couldn't work after burning out?

A research paper ("Long working hours increasing deaths from heart disease and stroke: WHO, ILO") published in 2021 by a team of scientists from the WHO and International Labour Organisation is a first global analysis of the loss of life and health associated with working long hours and it states some pretty shocking statistics.

They estimate that, in 2016, nearly 380,000 people died from stroke and 347,000 from heart disease as a result of having worked at least 55 hours a week, which is a staggering increase of 42 percent in heart disease and 19 percent by stroke due to working long hours. Put in more comparable terms- stress-induced heart disease and strokes caused by overwork are killing more people globally than Malaria!

And take another look at the number of hours worked that they were studying: it's 55!

How many people do you know that regularly work 55 hours or more every week?

Do you?

What could this be doing to your health?

And it is more damaging than we may think. The authors of the paper also claim that ill-health caused by work related stress and overwork is contributing to 23 million Disability adjusted lost years (DALY) i.e. lives shortened by health conditions or disabilities globally, shortening millions more lives.

If our work was causing more visible, physical, injuries, would we tolerate this?

No!

So why are we continuing to tolerate many hundreds of thousands of people being harmed by long hours and unmanaged workplace stress, when it is well-established that it causes significant long-term harm to our physical and mental health?

Finding Solutions

As a stress and resilience coach, I hear so many stories about my clients' employers not effectively dealing with the causes of chronic stress, leaving individuals with few options other than leaving their jobs to remove themselves from the stressors if they can't find ways to change their own response to them. Having experienced this as I shared previously, it causes more stress and resentment and reinforces the belief that it's the individual not the working arrangements that is the problem.

I created a free download listing ways of taming stress triggers, and some of these tools are detailed in later sections of this book, but if the burnout symptoms are due to workload or poor work organisation, and the employer is not taking action to address these areas, there is not a lot you can do other than step away from that organisation.

This, unfortunately, causes a lot of disruption and costs to both the employee and the employer, but it sadly may be your best option to start your recovery.

If any of these statements apply to you, then you may need to start thinking about a burnout escape strategy:

- Have you become cynical or critical at work?
- Do you drag yourself to work and have trouble getting started?
- Have you become irritable or impatient with co-workers, customers, or clients?
- Do you lack the energy to be consistently productive?
- Do you find it hard to concentrate?
- Do you lack satisfaction from your achievements?
- Do you feel disillusioned about your job?
- Are you using food, drugs, or alcohol to feel better or to simply not feel anything?
- Have your sleep habits changed?
- Are you troubled by unexplained headaches, stomach or bowel problems, or other physical complaints?

If you live in a country where it costs money to access medical care, how much are your insurance premiums going to be affected by a stress-induced illness? Or how much are the medical bills every time you have to seek treatment? And the scary bit is, once you have a mental-health- or stress-related illness on your medical record, you may not be covered for it after your first claim, and despite it being a discriminatory practice and illegal in the UK and other countries, if you declare a past episode of mental illness such as depression or anxiety related condition, some employers may assume that you are not a good prospect or will still be needing support, and will therefore not hire you.

Would they treat people with physical-health conditions like this? Probably not and it has been something that I have campaigned to change for many years here in the UK.

It is a sad fact that even though the job I was doing when I was caught up in burnout was working as a Health and Safety manager, there was still so much shame around admitting my own mental-health challenges. My employer still had a long way to go with their support structures and as already mentioned, I experienced discrimination and harassment when I challenged them about bullying behaviours. In fact, they used my past mental-health illness as a reason for my response to the bullying, blaming me instead of dealing with the perpetrator.

This fear of being 'found out', or seen as 'not coping' is the reason why so many people carry on working in toxic environments where stress is not being addressed or challenged. The organisational culture is not set up to adequately support them when they say it is affecting their health.

Too many skilled and experienced employees get 'moved on' or are forced to leave organisations due to harassment or bullying or not having their concerns heard and dealt with. This is such a high cost to pay for what could be a simple conversation and risk assessment to identify what needs to be done to reduce the exposure to the work-related stressors.

Instead, most companies simply choose to lose their investment in the employee's years of experience, skills, training, and customer knowledge and relationships , which often cannot be easily replaced. Not to mention the damage to reputation, the cost of recruiting and training new employees and the impact on the rest of the team who often have to pick up the work when colleagues leave. Plus, the remaining employees may be impacted by the loss of their team member and witnessing the behaviours that led to the person being driven out. Very often, the issues that cause one person to leave move on to the rest of the team, and a culture of fear and intimidation creeps in. This cannot be good for focus and productivity can it?

There are so many better ways of organising work to reduce fatigue and stress, and that is what I'll be sharing in the next chapter.

I am not alone in this initiative towards change. New UK guidelines were published in 2022 by the National Institute for Clinical Excellence (NICE) on supporting mental well-being at work.

They explain why their guidance is needed:

'Poor mental wellbeing costs employers an estimated £33 billion to £42 billion each year when staff struggle to perform, take more sick days and are more likely to leave.

In the UK, 15% of people at work are thought to have symptoms of an existing mental health problem. More needs to be done to create supportive workplaces where good mental wellbeing is valued.

Their key recommendations will come as no surprise, and I've included them in the next chapter. If you want to take a break from reading this and look them up before heading in to the next chapter, NICE have a resources page here (https:// www.nice.org.uk/guidance/ng212/resources), and a raft of evidence to support the benefits of supporting good mental wellbeing at work on their website here (https://www.nice.org. uk/guidance/ng212/evidence).

In the next chapter we're going to dive into the science of burnout and how we can address it in healthier ways.

Chapter 5
How Do We Burn Out?

"Burnout is about resentment.
Preventing it is about knowing yourself well enough to know
what it is you're giving up that makes you resentful."
—Marissa Mayer

Look at the Cause, not the Effect!

It is time to deal with the causes, not the symptoms, of chronic workplace stress.

To do so, we must drop the stigma around burnout and be clear on how burnout is created. As we have already established , it is recognised by the World Health Organisation (WHO) as a **workplace phenomenon,** not a medical condition. Here is a reminder of their definition:

"Burn-out is a syndrome conceptualised as resulting from chronic workplace stress that has not been successfully managed. It is characterised by three dimensions:

- *feelings of energy depletion or exhaustion;*
- *increased mental distance from one's job, or feelings of negativism or cynicism related to one's job; and*
- *reduced professional efficacy.*

Let's unpack that. Burnout results from "chronic workplace stress that has not been successfully managed."

What would you think of as *chronic workplace stress?*

Well according to the Merriam Webster Dictionary it can mean:

1a : continuing or occurring again and again for a long time...

2a: always present or encountered especially constantly vexing, weakening, or troubling (**Merriam-webster**)

So for stress to be ***chronic***, it is repeated for a long period of time, and as this definition says, can be weakening, troubling, or constantly vexing. I love that word, 'vexing', it has such a powerful sound when you say it and is a small word that means '*causing annoyance, frustration, or worry*', does this sound more familiar?

Workplace stress could be a wide variety of things, and to make understanding the mechanism of burnout even more difficult, our response to the stressors and coping abilities differ, depending on our previous experiences and current beliefs about our capacity or ability to deal with them.

Let's get clearer on what we mean by 'stress' as this word has become much misused and misunderstood. The definition of stress according to Merriam-Webster online dictionary is:

"a state resulting from a stress especially : one of bodily or mental tension resulting from factors that tend to alter an existent equilibrium". ("Stress Definition & Meaning")

Clear as mud, right? This is how the WHO explains it, and it makes things a bit clearer.

"Stress can be defined as any type of change that causes physical, emotional or psychological strain. Stress is your body's response to anything that requires attention or action. Everyone experiences stress to some degree. The way you respond to stress, however, makes a big difference to your overall well-being."

As we are looking at 'work related' stress, it might be good to explore this a bit more. The UK Health and Safety Executive (HSE) set out what the signs and causes of work-related stress are, and provide lots of resources that can help identify areas that can cause stress at work so the risk of psychological harm can be assessed. Best of all, they also lay out strategies on how to manage stressors to prevent harm to those who may be affected, and they describe six main areas that can lead to work-related stress if they are not managed properly. Similar frameworks have been developed in the European union ("Work-related stress: A guide")

These are:

1. Demands- are you able to cope with the demands of your job?,
2. Control- are you able to control the way you do your work?
3. Support- do you receive enough information and support at work?
4. Relationships- are you having trouble with relationships at work, or are you being bullied?
5. Role - do you fully understand your role and responsibilities?
6. Change- are you engaged and informed when your business is undergoing change such as restructuring or relocating? For example, if you are simply told when the change has happened without consultation, this may impact all of the areas above, but if you are consulted and included in the change process this gives you agency and a sense of ownership of the change process.

Looking back at my own story and applying these six categories it is so clear why I kept burning out, in the scientific research and laboratory manager roles I did, my job was pretty much to keep everything (and everyone) going in an environment where everyone else was stressed, causing friction in working relationships, and there was scant regard to understanding (or respecting) what my actual role and responsibilities were. The work was funded on short term contracts and staff were competing to publish results to secure further funding. I moved from this into a series of Health and Safety management roles which didn't help much in the 'relationships' area and increased demands even more as I tried to address a working culture that wasn't used to being told how to work safely and often resisted the invitation to do so!

What NICE work looks like.

Stress affects everyone differently – what causes one person to feel stressed may not affect another person in the same way. Factors like skills and experience, age or your health may all affect how you cope.

The big 'elephant in the room' that we need to address is how workers are treated when they report that they are experiencing burnout symptoms that are being caused (as we have learned earlier in this book) by workplace stress.

At the end of Chapter 3 there was a reflection question: How would your employer respond if you told them you were feeling burned out?

In my own, and many other people's experience, the reality is that the individual experiencing chronic stress at work is expected to either adjust their own response to the stressors, or more commonly, they are taken out of the environment where the stressors are present. The person is safe from the stressors, but the stressors do not get dealt with, so the destructive cycle goes on. This process is leaving a trail of damaged individuals, high staff turnover and lost productivity in companies around the world.

In my 20s, I had just got around to telling everyone at work that I was pregnant, and then a couple of weeks later I experienced a devastating miscarriage. At the time I didn't know that my coping mechanisms were low because of my PTSD (I wouldn't get that diagnosis for another 15 years!) so I pushed on through and returned to work only two weeks after losing the pregnancy, which in hindsight was far too early. This caused me to suffer a breakdown as I struggled with the grief and hormonal turmoil going on in my body.

I thought I had a brilliant boss at the time, but when I returned to work and told them I was feeling stressed at work and not coping well after the loss of my pregnancy, their response was 'it's your own fault you take too much on.'

I thought, *wow!* I couldn't believe they said that to me. However, due to my previous experiences of being abused at home all those years and being told I wasn't good enough, I just accepted it as truth as I was unable to face conflict or stand up for myself and call out these unacceptable comments.

Does a situation like that sound familiar to you?

If so, don't worry. There is a solution.

In Chapter 4, I mentioned the National Institute for Clinical Excellence (NICE) guidelines on supporting mental wellbeing at work and the huge costs that poor mental wellbeing leads to in lost time and reduced productivity each year.

If the right support is not in place for reporting the impacts of stress on your mental wellbeing, it could cause your mental health to be further affected and lead to a more long-term illness and burnout. This is what happened in my case, and in many other stories I've heard in the years I've been raising awareness of mental health at work.

Whilst my mental health challenges after my lost pregnancy may not have been entirely caused by workplace stress, it was still the main issue that impacted my mental health and as my employer effectively blamed me for feeling unable to cope with the grief on top of my workload, and there was no attempt to review it or make adjustments to allow me to process or heal.

NICE's guidelines recommend supporting mental well-being at work by adopting a three-tiered approach (National Institute for Clinical Excellence):

1. Organisational-level approaches, setting a foundation for good mental well-being
2. Individual approaches - making sure that individuals get the support they need and
3. Targeted approaches - to address specific issues or challenges.

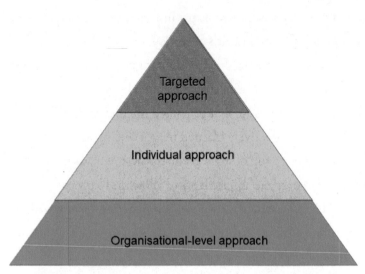

Tiered approach to mental wellbeing in the workplace

Let's look at some examples of actions that could be used to support your mental well-being at work to protect from the type of stress that can lead to burnout.

Organisational Approaches

First and foremost, the NICE guidelines suggest that organisations take a <u>preventive</u> and more <u>proactive</u> strategic approach to mental well-being at work by actively promoting mental well-being *before* harm can occur. They can do this by ensuring that mental well-being and psychological safety is embedded in the overall business strategy of organisational policies and practices.

This could include reviewing:

- Workplace culture (including how 'banter' and language around mental health is used)
- Workload (too much and too little!)
- Job quality and role autonomy
- Addressing concerns that employers and employees may have about mental health, including stigma around disclosing any issues

It's also important to make sure that stress and psychological harm are considered in your work-related risk assessments, and if any risks are identified, your employer takes proactive steps to address the risks, so if you are having any conversations with your employer about experiencing burnout, requesting a review of the stress risk assessments for your work is a good place to start.

Individual measures

When considering individual measures for reducing stress and psychological harm, it is important to ensure that factors outside of work which might be influencing your mental well-being are considered in the risk assessments. For example, parents, carers, or those with low income or multiple jobs may be more vulnerable to stress and burnout to those with less demands on their non-working time.

Another way could be to use a mental well-being measure to identify when someone may be in need of additional support, then to signpost them to the service that best meets their needs. There are lots of ways you can measure your mental wellbeing, this could be a simple verbal check-in or numerical score in a journal or app.

Some examples of validated measures include What Works Wellbeing's workplace well-being questionnaire (Tenaglia) or the Warwick Medical School's Warwick-Edinburgh Mental Wellbeing Scales question set (WEMWBS) developed by the NHS in association with Edinburgh and Warwick Universities. This is a fourteen-question scale that has been used internationally, covering a range of wellbeing areas that can be 'scored' to measure overall well-being and to evaluate health and well-being projects and population mental wellness.(Brown et al.)

However you measure, it is important to ensure that this is done in confidence and without stigma or judgement around the result, and if support is indicated as needed, there are options to signpost to what is the right type for your needs.

Moral Injury

In 2009 another type of psychological harm that leads to burnout was recognised. **Moral Injury** refers to *the lasting strong cognitive and emotional response that is caused by performing, witnessing, or failing to prevent an action that violates your own moral beliefs and expectations* (Litz et al.) .

Moral injury is a concept developed by psychiatrist Jonathan Shay (Shay, 1994, Shay 2002) as a result of his clinical work with military personnel which sought to separate

PTSD from the complex social and political elements of experiences of work and the feelings of betrayal by leaders when being asked to work with inadequate equipment, being given an unreasonable distribution of duties and being sent into danger zones when the leadership giving orders were in safe and secure locations. Shay defined moral injury as *"A betrayal of what's right, by someone who holds legitimate authority* (e.g., in the military – a leader), *in a high-stakes situation"* (Shay).

Other studies have looked at a range of professions including firefighters, police, emergency services, journalism, vets, and the clergy (Williamson et al.) and found significant associations between moral injury and PTSD and depression, which could lead to burnout. A 2022 review by the University of Sheffield management school (Lewis et al.) looked at business settings and found a common pattern of how moral injury develops:

- Stage 1: The event - which could be an action (or inaction) by employers or colleagues that challenges the individual's moral beliefs or expectations about how they should be treated in their role. This could include discrimination, harassment, 'breaking the rules' at work, bullying, or failing in their duty of care to them or the people they serve.

- Stage 2: Initial reaction - This could be a range of emotional responses including shock, fear, shame, guilt, and anger depending on the event and the individual's emotional state. Other responses could include reporting to their employer or reacting to the individuals causing the unacceptable behaviour, evidence gathering or removing themselves from the situation to enable them to process the experience.

- Stage 3: Reflection and processing - The researchers found that many of their respondents experienced a predictable lack of response from their employer when reporting concerns about incidents, so they went into a period of reflection and processing, commonly experiencing feelings of frustration and a lack of control over their work and how they were treated. This can develop into a cognitive dissonance between wanting to do a good job and the need to feel safe and valued as an employee, so unless the situation can be adequately resolved, it can trigger the stress response and develop into mental- and physical-health issues like we have described earlier in this book.

- Stage 4: Taking action - Typical actions taken by employees experiencing moral injury taking part in the Sheffield study included leaving the organisation, starting their own business, or taking time out to recover. Others took some form of 'correction action' including seeking professional support (which we will look at in Chapters 8 and 9), or shut down emotionally to protect themselves from further harm.

Do any of these responses resonate with you? What actions have you taken in response to not having your values and support needs met at work?

Let's look at some more targeted actions that could support you if you are experiencing stress or moral injury at work.

Targeted measures

Examples of targeted interventions to support mental well-being at work could be to work with individuals who are at risk of, or who have already disclosed that they have experienced moral injury or mental health challenges, to develop with them an individualised well-being plan with adjustments to their work that supports their current coping abilities.

This could include;

- dealing with expectations around your role,
- reducing hours,
- flexibility on timings to accommodate caring or health-related commitments, or
- providing a peer mentor who can check in and support you.
- Most importantly in this approach is to identify any work related stressors not dealt with at an organisational level that need to be addressed, and reduce exposure to them.

Employers Legal Duties

OK, so I'm going to start this section with a disclaimer: I am in no way a qualified lawyer or legal expert, but I am going to share some examples of how legislation in the UK and some other countries are set up to protect workers from conditions that can affect their mental health and can cause the chronic stress that leads to burnout.

As we have learned in this book, burnout is caused by **unmanaged workplace stress,** so if you are going to tackle it, you need to start some difficult conversations at work about how the stressors can be better managed, or better still, eliminated.

If you work for an organisation that has a supportive human resources or occupational health team then this conversation might be relatively straightforward. They should have policies and risk assessments for workplace stress that you could review together. They should be able to help you work out ways of dealing with the stressors that you have identified.

However, if the causes of stress are related to the organisation, the relationships with your team or the workload, then this may not be so easy to resolve and you might need to get help outside of your organisation. If you are a member of a trade union, professional body, or trade body, you might be able to find support or guidance there. Or you could try a citizen's advice or employment mediation organisation to advise you.

Let's go back to the **World Health Organisation** definition of burnout, which is:

"Burnout is a syndrome conceptualised as resulting from chronic workplace stress that has not been successfully managed."

Let's break this down into what an employer's duty of care is to protect their employees from harm.

- Legislation under the European framework directive 89/391 requires that all employers have a "duty to ensure the safety and health of workers in every aspect related to work" in so far as they entail a risk to health and safety. This duty covers work-related stress and its causes.

- In the United States, workplace safety regulations require employers to '*Provide a workplace free from serious recognized hazards and comply with standards, rules and regulations issued under the OSH Act.*' ("Employer Responsibilities")

- In the UK, the Health & Safety at Work etc Act 1974 requires employers to secure the health (including mental health), safety and welfare of employees whilst at work, meaning that in the UK employers have a legal duty to protect workers from stress at work by doing a risk assessment to identify anything that could cause psychological harm and acting on it.

- International Standard ISO 45003 is the first global standard giving practical guidance on managing psychological health in the workplace. Whilst not legally binding, it provides evidence based best practice guidance on the management of psychosocial risk and offers examples of effective actions that can be taken to manage these to support employee wellbeing. ("ISO 45003:2021 - Occupational health and safety management – Psychological health and safety at work – Guidelines for managing psychosocial risks")

While the NICE resources and Stress management standards described in this chapter are a great place to start, based on current practice, additional resources may be needed for the following:

- To ensure an inclusive workplace environment and culture to support mental well-being. This may involve providing staff with facilities such as private access to the internet and IT equipment for remotely delivered interventions. It could also include licensing costs for use of validated tools to measure mental well-being.
- Implementing organisation-wide approaches for responding to unexpected traumatic events affecting employees, such as a pandemic or terrorist attack. Also offering staff additional support after an occupational traumatic event such as an assault or death of a colleague.
- Training and support for managers to equip them with the knowledge, tools, skills, and resources to improve awareness and promote mental well-being at work. This includes staff training and time to develop, deliver and monitor policies, and raising awareness to

ensure policies are translated into practice across the organisation.

- Supporting staff to access individual-level approaches to mental well-being such as mindfulness, yoga or meditation classes, for example by protecting rest breaks or allowing time off or financial support to attend sessions.

- Offering or providing access to therapies including allowing time off and funding for employees to attend support sessions. This may be difficult for some organisations to support during work hours for financial and operational reasons, so it may be better to provide opportunities to access sessions outside work hours rather than not making them available at all.

- Providing flexible working hours or changes to the job or workplace to minimise any risks to mental well-being

Difficult conversations at work

So, with what you have already learned in this book, and armed with your circles of support (we'll talk about these in Chapter 8) and any information or diagnoses from the professionals you may have sought help from (see Chapter 9), you can be ready to tackle dealing with your employer and working with them to address their legal obligations to protect you from work-related stress.

Talking things out with your employer is important to ensure that they understand the impact that your working conditions are having on your health. Before you do this consider these questions:

- What experiences have contributed to your stress at work? Make a note with dates and as much detail as you can.

- What policies or procedures are in place to address the stresses you are experiencing? Make sure you have access to a copy and highlight the areas that are relevant.

- Check your workplace employee benefits to see what medical professional help you can access.

- If you have contacted your doctor about your symptoms, you might need to let your employer know.

If you manage to get to have a conversation and want some examples of good practice here are a few that you might like to suggest to your employer:

- A dating app company (Bumble) gave everyone a paid week off work to rest after a busy year trading and building their company – recognising that burnout was a concern amongst their workforce. (Jones and Jordan) This is a nice gesture to help reset, but as we have already learned, might not be good enough if workload and other stress factors are not dealt with after the short break.

- Trained mentors or listening teams can get help to people before they reach a crisis stage. Sometimes people can recognise that they are coming into a period of burnout and can talk about it and manage it if the right support is there.

- If people do get to the stage where they need time off, when they're off, it's important not to pressurise them to come back to work before they're ready. Many people don't understand that burnout isn't just psychological, it's physical as well. It's your body telling you, 'you need to slow down and heal', and the time required for this process can vary depending on the individual and the extent that their energy and coping reserves have been depleted.

- Employers need to understand the individual reporting a problem and really *listen* to them. Their experience of burnout could be completely different to somebody else's, and their return to work process might need to be completely different too.

- And, probably the most important thing to remember is to review the causes of the stress and take steps to address them before the person comes back to work.

Supporting a colleague experiencing burnout

What can we all do as colleagues to support people close to us who might be going through a difficult time or feeling burned out?

73

A really simple habit to get into is to **ask twice** when we check in with each other. It is easy to ask, 'are you okay?' and the standard response is 'I'm fine' and we accept it without question. However, the person you're asking might not be fine, but they don't feel they can go into detail, or they might not want to burden anyone with their issues. If you ask the question again: "are you really okay?" It gives them an opportunity to open up knowing that you actually want to listen.

What is important is to listen to them and their support needs whilst protecting your own boundaries on time and energy. If the work stresses are affecting you too, then it might be helpful to work with the colleague to find a way to bring it to your employer's attention as it is less easy for them to ignore the issue or blame individuals if multiple employees are saying the same thing. A great analogy I heard in a webinar on management of workplace stress was this: if you have a pond and one fish gets sick then you treat the fish, however if more fish get sick then the issue is with the water in the pond and that is what needs treatment, not the fish!

If a colleague has to take time off work due to their burnout symptoms, it's important to keep in contact with them in a way that meets their support needs as the longer they are away from work, the more difficult it will be for them to return.

Burn-Brighter Step:

How does your workplace measure up against the NICE and stress management guidelines described in this chapter?

- Make a list in your journal of the organisational measures to address stress including policies and cultural practices in the way your work is organised. Are you familiar with them?
- How about stress risk assessments? Have you seen or done one?
- Are you able to discuss or amend your working arrangements if you need adjustments to support you? Who might you talk to to find out?

Chapter 6

I Am An Ace Survivor —
Are You?

The NICE techniques and legal frameworks around risk assessment for managing work-related stress are a good start. But what difference could we create if we took a more trauma-informed approach to stress management, and considered the impact that Adverse Childhood Experiences (ACE's) have on individuals and their ability to deal with stress in their adult lives? This would fundamentally alter how the risk-assessment processes for stress are dealt with by employers and could help reduce the stigma that many burned out individuals feel.

In Chapter 1, I shared some of my story of how my early experiences have impacted my mental health and shaped my ability to respond to work and life challenges. Learning to understand and accept this has played a key part in my recovery and breaking free from burnout so let's explore how this could help you.

Adverse Childhood Experiences (ACEs) are events that occur in childhood that are potentially traumatic. These could include experiencing or witnessing; violence, abuse, family mental health or substance use, family breakdown or imprisonment, homelessness, food insecurity, racism, or other forms of discrimination.

These conditions can all contribute to what is described as **toxic stress** and evidence has shown that this can have long term impacts on brain development, our ability to form healthy relationships as well as our health and wellbeing. So it is clear to see how this might affect how you show up in the workplace and deal with your job!

A large body of evidence shows that experiencing traumatic challenges as children can affect us into adulthood. ACEs can happen to anyone, regardless of their social, economic or gender status, although the number of ACEs tends to increase with a decrease in living standards and community connection. Recent studies from Blackburn & Darwen borough council ("Childhood trauma") and other research including a National household survey of adverse childhood experiences and their relationship with resilience to health-harming behaviours in England (Lowey) have shown that:

- Nearly half of people in England experience at least one ACE, with around 9 percent experiencing four or more ACEs – or put another way, for every 100 adults in England, 48 have suffered at least one ACE during their childhood and nine have suffered four or more.

- Experiencing six or more ACEs can reduce your life expectancy by 20 years!

The original ACEs study was conducted in the United States, where researchers surveyed 17,000 individuals. They found that around 64 percent of the respondents reported at least one ACE, with over a quarter (26 percent) suffering physical abuse. Around 13 percent had experienced four or more ACEs. (Felitti, et al #)

The Centres for Disease Control (CDC) suggest that preventing ACEs could potentially reduce a large number of health conditions including burnout. For example, they claim that up to 1.9 million cases of heart disease and 21 million cases of depression could have been potentially avoided by preventing ACEs ("Adverse Childhood Experiences (ACEs)"). If you think you may be an ACE survivor, the CDC website has a great resource page here https://www.cdc.gov/violenceprevention/aces/ .

There are significant financial and human costs involved here- the CDC estimates that the economic and social costs to families, communities, and society totals hundreds of billions of dollars each year.

ACEs can have lasting, negative effects on health, well-being, affecting emotional and social development and behaviour – thus impacting life opportunities such as education and job potential. These experiences can increase the risks of injury, risk-taking behaviours and self-harm as well as child health and safeguarding problems as well as a wide range of chronic diseases and leading causes of death such as cancer, diabetes, heart disease, and suicide.

An article in psychology today (Golden) discusses the impact of ACE's on Adult anger and another in the same journal (Golden) discusses the links between perfectionism and ACE's. Survivors striving to be 'perfect' due to trauma from experiencing ACE's tend to direct anger at themselves and others when, inevitably, perfection proves to be impossible. This, unsurprisingly, causes difficulties in both work and social relationships.

Understanding the impact of these developmental traumas could improve working relationships and team dynamics, as being open to the possibility that our co-workers are behaving in response to unprocessed trauma instead of snootiness or bossiness can result in more compassion and understanding—and can even result in both parties finding a solution that everyone is satisfied with.

ACEs and other social determinants of health listed in the infographic below from public health England can cause what is described as 'toxic stress,' or extended or prolonged stress.

The CDC study (Felitti, et al.) reported that Toxic stress from ACEs can change brain development and affect such things as attention, decision-making, learning, and response to stress. This might have a significant impact on adult survivors' lives and their potential to perform at work, and make them more vulnerable to burnout.

The researchers also found that children growing up with toxic stress may have difficulty forming healthy and stable relationships. Toxic stress may also result in unstable work histories as adults and struggles with finances, jobs, and depression throughout life. Worse, these effects can also be passed on to their own children. This means some children may face further exposure to toxic stress from historical and ongoing family trauma. For example, this could be due to a family being trapped in a cycle of poverty resulting from the limited educational and economic opportunities of their parents.

I have mentioned throughout this book my experience of ACEs and the impact they had on my mental health and ability to deal with stress at work. I haven't mentioned the key incidents that led to me developing PTSD, and I have to include here a **trigger warning** for anyone who has experienced violence or assault.

I already mentioned that my step-family and mother subjected me to a whole range of alienation behaviours during the custody battle between my parents after my mum took me away from my dad when I was five years old. For the next decade, I heard constant criticism of my father and his family leading me to develop feelings of 'not belonging' in either family as I spent time in both places on custody visits. However, as my mother's mental health deteriorated and her alcohol dependence grew, I became the target of more emotional and physical abuse when she wasn't coping or was angry with my stepdad or wanted to get at my dad through me.

One day, when I was around 15 years old (I don't remember the exact date as my brain has protected me from the full memory of the event), this erupted into a situation where she flipped and attacked me, grabbing a knife and chasing me around the house causing me to lock myself in the downstairs cloakroom as she tried to bash the door in to get to me. My toddler and baby half-sisters witnessed this, and my stepdad had to pin her against the wall to disarm her and allow me to grab my sisters and escape to the car parked at the back of the house. He drove us to the safety of our aunt's house before calling the ambulance to get my mother sectioned.

This incident, not surprisingly, had a significant impact on our whole family, causing me to move into a state of permanent hypervigilance, as the person who was supposed to be my caregiver had tried to take my life. What caused the most damage, and has taken me so long to recover from however, was that even though my mother was sectioned and treated for her mental health issues, me and my sisters were sent back home to live with her and my stepdad with no support or intervention from social services or therapists, and just left to get on with it.

The emotional abuse and violent outbursts continued through my teens until I left home after my step dad kicked me out when I walked in on another argument between him and my mother. I was 17, and in the middle of studies for my A-levels and was faced with the choice of giving up my studies and moving 200 miles away to live with my father and his new family, or staying with another relative for a year to finish school, but still be exposed to the perpetrators of the abuse who visited every weekend.

I chose to complete my studies and bottle up my anger and other emotions to stick out my schooling so I could escape to university. This, not surprisingly added to my trauma and feelings of rejection, not feeling 'good enough', and very low self-worth, leading me to decades of overwork, people-pleasing and perfectionism as I constantly strived to achieve more and not allow myself any time to sit with the emotional fallout of these experiences.

This story is not something that I was able to talk about with many people for many years, until I found the right therapy to help me remove the emotional charge from retelling it, as I couldn't talk about it without becoming retraumatised, so it would not be something that I would have been able to share with any employer (or indeed want to share widely). This had a significant impact on my ability to form working relationships (especially with female authority figures) and deal with confrontation or challenges in the jobs that I did as I was trapped in the fear state with my amygdala on overdrive most of the time, triggered by phone calls, emails, and even raised voices or news stories about violence or abuse.

This is why I am so passionate about workplaces and schools adopting a more trauma-informed approach to dealing with ACE survivors.

If it was acknowledged that they need support to deal with the potential physical- and mental-health consequences of their past experiences without feeling shame or stigma about this, perhaps more people might seek help? Even better, if schools and other public and health services were trained to be more trauma-informed when dealing with young people experiencing abuse, family trauma or violence at home, the emotional support could be put in place to enable them to process and recover before they start work?

How to be an ACE informed workplace

A good place to start is screening for ACEs, so those with ACEs are aware of it and can begin the healing process.

Does your employee support package include screening for ACES, or offer effective support for those who identify as ACE or abuse survivors?

If 9 percent of the workforce are likely to have suffered four or more ACE's, and nearly 50 percent of the population have experienced at least one ACE, then it would make huge economic (and ethical) sense to equip us with emotional-intelligence and resilience-support tools!

We need to educate ourselves and each other on safe ways to release the trauma and associated physical and mental health impacts that ACEs cause. There are many ways to do this, you will learn some of the ways you can do this in Chapters 8 and 9.

The first step is to remove the stigma of asking for help, and acknowledging your experiences in a confidential and non-judgemental space. If we could share better ways to allow all ACE survivors to understand that they are not ill, weak, useless, or failures, but are living with the toxic burden of unheard and unresolved trauma that is impacting their bodies and minds, the world would be a much healthier place.

So, if you are feeling burnout, you are not weak or crazy—but you may have experienced ACEs that could have made you far more vulnerable to burning out, and it is time to find some support to help you process that. In the rest of this book, you will learn some of the tools and support that can be used, but skip ahead to Chapter 8 if you need to find that now.

Burn-Brighter Step:

Note down in your journal a timeline of the first two decades of your life and record any experiences that might be classed as ACEs. These may include:

- experiencing violence, abuse, or neglect
- witnessing violence in the home or community
- having a family member attempt or die by suicide.
- growing up in a household with a family member with substance use problems, mental health problems or separation due to divorce or being in custody/prison.
- growing up in a racially segregated community, low income household
- experiencing food or housing insecurity

You can get creative with this and draw them as a river, with each experience placed as a rock in the stream, or as a ladder with a rung for each decade and the experiences notched on the supports between them. Or simply draw a line and divide it by decade and note your significant life experiences. This may bring up some strong emotions for you, so be gentle, set aside some quiet time to do it and make sure you give yourself time and space to reflect afterwards.

Chapter 7

When to Get Help

'There will always be too much to do – and this realisation is liberating. Today more than ever, there's just no reason to assume any fit between the demands on your time – all the things you would like to do, or feel you ought to do – and the amount of time available. 'Thanks to capitalism, technology and human ambition, these demands keep increasing, while your capacities remain largely fixed. It follows that the attempt to "get on top of everything" is doomed. (Indeed, it's worse than that – the more tasks you get done, the more you'll generate.)

—Oliver Burkeman (Burkeman)

Now that you understand how and why you are feeling burned out, the next step is to find the right support to help you break free and recover. This is probably the most difficult chapter in this book for me to write, as the simple answer is that doing this will look different for everyone!

Before diving into what type of support you need, first, let's determine if you need support for your burnout at all. Let's start by reminding ourselves of Professor Maslach's description of burnout as *'a psychological syndrome emerging as a prolonged response to chronic interpersonal stressors on the job'* (Maslach, et al.).

The three key elements she described in this response are:

1. Overwhelming feelings of exhaustion, also described as wearing out, loss of energy, depletion, debilitation, and fatigue.
2. Feelings of cynicism and detachment from the job, including depersonalization, negative or inappropriate attitudes towards clients, irritability, loss of idealism, and withdrawal.
3. A sense of ineffectiveness and lack of accomplishment, reduced productivity or capability, low morale, and an inability to cope. (Maslach, et al.)

So if you are feeling any of the feelings in the list above, it could be time for you to get some support from a medical professional to see if you are experiencing burnout.

Burnout or Depression?

It is important here to distinguish between burnout and other mental-health conditions such as Depression, and this needs to be done by a medical professional (not Dr Google or your mates on social media!)

Because the symptoms of burnout and depression are quite similar they are frequently confused, so people reporting experiences of burnout may be given a depression diagnosis and given antidepressant medications, or people who are depressed are diagnosed with burnout and told to simply take time off work or 'slow down'.

As burnout is caused by **unmanaged workplace stress**, the traditional depression treatment is not going to help if you are burned out. Antidepressants do not take the workplace stress away and all a depression misdiagnosis will do in this instance is shift the focus for action onto the individual experiencing burnout. It does not point at work as being the problem; rather, it blames the individual's mental health for their 'not being able to cope' or in some way being weak when what they really need is a change in working practices and the right support to get back into work when (or if) they are ready to return.

Similarly, if you are experiencing depression, you need access to the right psychological or psychiatric support (including medication if appropriate), and not just an extended holiday. The various treatments for depression are very different from those for burnout, so a professional diagnosis is the first best step towards proper recovery.

Some symptoms of depression that are not typical of burnout include

- low self-esteem,
- hopelessness, and
- thinking about killing yourself.

If you are experiencing these thoughts relating to areas of your life outside of your work, you may have depression or another mental health condition that needs professional support, so it is important to get an appointment as soon as you can. Depression could develop as a result of burnout, but this is not always the case. Having access to a medical professional that is informed about these distinctions is the key in getting the treatment that is right for you yet so many people either do not seek treatment or get fobbed off with inadequate diagnoses due to immense pressures and under resourcing of the healthcare system and a lack of training and awareness of the occupational health elements of the symptoms people are reporting.

Measuring burnout

If you want to quantify how burned out you are feeling (this may be the case if you are considering going to see a medical professional) there are a number of measures that can be used.

The first one was designed to assess all three different dimensions of the burnout experience based on psychometric research by Prof Christina Maslach and her team, and was thus named the **Maslach Burnout inventory** (Maslach, et al.).

This has been the major tool in burnout research and has been used since its publication in 1981 and validated globally after being translated into many different languages and tested on people in a range of occupations. (Maslach and Jackson),

It is a set of 22-25 questions including statements about emotional exhaustion, depersonalisation, personal accomplishment, and involvement in your work, rated on two dimensions: frequency and intensity.

Another measure is the **Bergen Burnout inventory** (BBI) which also measures the three areas of burnout: (FeLDT et al.).

*   exhaustion at work,
*   cynicism about your work, and
*   feelings of inadequacy/unproductivity at work.

A third measure you may come across is the **Oldenberg Burnout Inventory** (OBI), which was developed to address some of the psychometric limitations of the Maslach scale as well as the limited scope of burnout upon which it is based. As a result, Demerouti *et al.* have developed the OBI as an alternative measure of burnout. This measurement tool looks at the exhaustion and disengagement at work elements of burnout.

Other measures that may be used include,

*   the **Shirom-Melamed Burnout Measure** (SMBM) which looks at the differences between physical, cognitive and emotional exhaustion, and
*   the **Copenhagen Burnout Inventory** (CBI) which consists of three scales measuring *personal burnout, work-related burnout, and client-related burnout,* for use in different work domains. (Tage et al.)

So whatever measure you are given by a medical or other professional or choose to do on your own, let's say you determine that you are burnt out, what next?

That is what the rest of this book is about, so read on to discover how to begin your recovery journey and address the causes of your burnout so you can burn brighter and never burn out again.

Burn-Brighter Step:

Take a look at the typical symptoms of chronic stress below and see how likely you are to be experiencing burnout.

- Feeling overwhelmed.
- Having racing thoughts or difficulty concentrating at work that spills over into your home life.
- Feeling irritable with work colleagues and your friends and family.
- Feel constantly worried, anxious, or scared.
- Reduced self-confidence.
- Feeling tired all the time and having difficulty sleeping (this could have a number of causes so needs to be taken in context with all the other symptoms and physical causes ruled out by a medical professional).
- Avoiding things or people you are having problems with, avoiding conflict.

- Changes in your eating habits, eating more or less than usual.
- Self-medicating with alcohol, cigarettes, or other substances.

If you are ticking most of these boxes then you may be experiencing burnout, and you need to get some support. Chapters 8 and 9 will guide you through how to do this and who you might like to reach out to. If you are booking an appointment with a medical professional you could take your notes from your journal with you to the appointment. Ask the professional to walk you through one or more of the burnout measuring tools described above. In Chapter 10, you'll learn some tools to help you turn the tables on burnout for good.

Chapter 8

How To Get Help Part 1: Accept And Connect

"You may not control all the events that happen to you, but you can decide not to be reduced by them."
—Maya Angelou

If you have identified that you are experiencing stress and feeling burnout, the first thing to do is to drop the shame!

In the previous chapters of this book I have shared some of my path to recovery from burnout and PTSD caused by Adverse Childhood Experiences (ACES) and we have also learned how it is important to adopt a trauma-informed approach in any situation when you are trying to change a behaviour or set of beliefs to enable change to happen.

It is really important to be present and connect with how tired you are feeling. Being low on energy and lacking interest in your work is not helped by feeling shame, anxiety, or guilt about it. Anyone who has ever tried scuba-diving will know that when they are low on air, the first thing they need to do is to calm their breathing so they can preserve their remaining supplies as they make their controlled ascent.

So, as a first step towards your recovery, try simply accepting how you feel. Yes, it sounds simple but if you have been ruled for your whole life by the 'shoulds' and 'coulds' around your emotional self, this can be a big deal! If you have never done this before, it is not difficult, just sit with your breath, close your eyes if you want to (making sure you are in a safe place and not operating heavy machinery or driving at this point!) and tune into your body to check in with where you are feeling most fatigued. This may be a generalised feeling all over your body, or it may show up in a specific area, like your shoulders, chest, or head. The act of focussing on these areas of tension, whilst slowing your breathing can sometimes be enough to bring release of some of the stress you are holding (you'll learn more about this in Chapter 9!)

Embedded with every stress is a meaning that we assign to it. If you can acknowledge and address the meaning, you don't get the same level of stress response. Try this:

- Acknowledge the stress, for example, an extra project that just landed in your inbox.
- Work out why the stress matters, why it is happening. What meaning are you giving to the stress? This is your 'tabletop' that we learned about in Chapter 3. Using the additional project example, this could be the stories you are telling yourself about that, what it might take from you to complete it, and the

consequences of not completing it to the standard you (or your manager) expect.

- Then you can work out how to deal with each aspect of these stories you assign to the stress trigger. We'll learn some really helpful tools in the next few sections!

Researchers have found that there was a 23-percent reduction in the physical symptoms of stress (headaches etc) when subjects removed the meaning of the stress (D'souza et al.). So, in the example given above, if your stories about the additional project included fears about losing your job if you didn't get it done , or not having time to complete the project and having to miss out on family events, or some other stories that equated your self-worth with getting the project done, then this gives the project extra meaning and power over your thinking, triggering your stress response and the cascade of physical and mental effects that come with it.

If however, you approached the extra project as another task that needed to be slotted into your schedule and did not assign any personal worth meanings to getting it done, your response would be less emotionally intense, and, depending on the nature of the project and how it was presented to you by your manager, it could even spark more positive emotional responses such as excitement, curiosity and gratitude.

So, as we have shown here, the same trigger or event can impact individuals in different ways, depending on their state of mind, past experiences and the meaning they assign to it.

In his ground-breaking book 'The body keeps the score' Bessel Van der Kolk, (2015) wrote:

'Our great challenge is to apply the lessons of neuroplasticity, the flexibility of brain circuits, to rewire the brains and reorganise the minds of people who have been programmed by life itself to experience others as threats and themselves as helpless.' (Van der Kolk)

He also wrote.

'There are real neurological reasons why those exposed to high doses of adversity are more likely to engage in high-risk behaviours.' (Van der Kolk)

For 'high-risk behaviours' you can substitute 'hypervigilance', 'perfectionism', 'people pleasing' and 'low self-esteem' too. We can't begin to consider how you can deal with the chronic stress that is causing you to burnout without considering whether you have experienced trauma.

In fact, the issues that are triggering the stress response in you may be traumas themselves, for example, having to give a presentation or take part in a performance review with senior management. For people who have experienced bullying or other forms of emotional abuse in their early lives, a belief may have formed that they must avoid criticism or being visible, so if the presentation or review is not conducted in a psychologically safe setting, it could be very traumatising for them to do. Similarly, if someone has experienced abuse or trauma with a role model of a certain gender or level of seniority, they may experience difficulty relating to colleagues of the same gender or authority level at work as it triggers memories of the original abuse. The cumulative effect of all this on your mental and physical health are what you are experiencing in burnout.

This book is not intended as a therapy guide, so I'm not going to go into too much detail here about the therapeutic options for you if you are experiencing burnout. That said, it is important to consider what option may be right for you and to know that treatment will help you build the foundation of resilience you need when dealing with the workplace stress that is causing you to burnout. Chapter 9 will help you consider what type of professional may be best suited to support you.

Circles of support

Did you know that when you look at a hill on your own it looks steeper than when you look at it with others? (Schnall et al.)

Researchers found that experimental participants who were accompanied by a friend estimated an image of a hill shown to them to be less steep than participants who were looking at the image on their own. They went on to discover that just thinking of someone who was supportive whilst looking at an image of a hill made it appear less steep than when they thought of a neutral person or someone they didn't like! (Schnall et al.)

Social connection is very important – the people we surround ourselves with can give us confidence, support, and the love we need to overcome difficulties in life. This can be just as important (if not, more important) than professional help and workplace changes when it comes to overcoming burnout and other mental-health issues. How connected do you feel?

In 1935, a species of firefly was discovered that lights up simultaneously in a group when looking for a mate. The researcher who made the discovery got the sack as no one believed him – but many years later he was proved right and it was shown that these insects had an 82-percent success rate at finding a mate compared to a 3-percent rate when they lit up individually. (Moiseff and Copeland).

But what has this got to do with burnout? Apart from the nice analogy of burning brighter together, it shows that an energetic process such as finding a mate can be made much easier with the support of your community. So can beating burnout, as you can find ways of avoiding or dealing more healthily with the work-related stress if you have a supportive network and don't feel like you are dealing with the stressors on your own.

So let's look at your network and see how it can support you:

- How would you rate your social life?
- Do you have a good social support network?
- Do you manage to keep in touch with family and friends enough to meet your needs?
- How could you make more time to connect with friends and family this week?

In 1943 Abraham Maslow published a theory of the human hierarchy of needs, and this was further developed in his book *__Motivation and Personality__* in 1954 (Maslow). This has been the basis of many more sociological theories of Human happiness and fulfilment.

In *Motivation and Personality*, (Maslow) Maslow argued that, in order for individuals to thrive and excel, once our basic survival needs for food, water, shelter, rest, safety and security are met, we need to develop a culture that supports our psychological needs including feeling like we belong and we are loved. After this we need self-esteem, a sense of achievement and to understand our place in the society we live in for self-fulfilment. The widely used pyramid diagram shown below illustrates this separated into our deficiency needs (if they are not met we can't survive or thrive), and our growth needs (if we meet these we move into personal growth and challenge to higher levels of purpose):

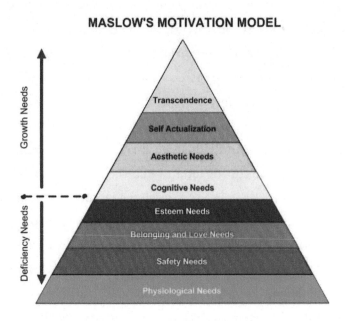

Later in 1973, John Bowlby developed a theory on attachment (Bowlby), realising that human beings of all ages are found to be at their happiest and to be able to function at their best when they are confident that they have a trusted support network. This provides a sense of safety and security, so if the person has not experienced anyone in their life who fits this role, or their main caregiver(s) has in some way caused them harm, they may not have a healthy framework to model relationships in their adult life.

From both models, it is clear that good social connections are essential to our mental and physical health and our overall well-being. Social isolation and loneliness are often the first signs that you are experiencing burnout as you become too exhausted to keep up with social engagements or stay connected with family and friends. Or, as was my own experience, these very connections may even contribute to the mental load in addition to the work stresses you may be experiencing.

In global health policy, social isolation and loneliness are increasingly being recognised as a priority public health problem as both are so widespread. The World health Organisation claims that 20–34 percent of older people in China, Europe, Latin America, and the United States of America are lonely, and a study by the health foundation in the UK found that one in five 16–24-year-olds reported that they often feel lonely. (Dearing) ("Social Isolation and Loneliness - Social Isolation and Loneliness")

Connecting beyond your inner circle:

Did you know that having diverse social connections predicts how long we live, and even impacts how resistant we are to catching colds? (Valtorta et al.) Researchers have estimated that the effect of loneliness on life expectancy can be the same as smoking thirteen cigarettes a day! (Howick et al.)

Our broader social networks provide a sense of belonging and influence how safe and secure we feel. Building connections in our local community contributes to our own happiness and that of those around us, enabling our communities to flourish. (Marmot)

Research has shown that happiness is contagious across social networks. (Marmot). Our happiness depends not only on the happiness of those in our direct social network, but on the happiness of the people they know too. In other words, happiness ripples out through groups of people, like a pebble thrown into a pond. So, if you want to start changing the way you respond to your work, it would really help if you strengthened your connections with your social network and tuned into those people you hang out with most. Are they feeling the same way as you about work, or are they energised and feeling more balanced in their lives?

If the people you spend most time with are in the first category, then it is likely that you will find it difficult to see a way out of the situation you are in and it might be time to think about who you spend your precious time with.

How can you start thinking about connecting beyond your existing 'tribe' with people who might uplift, support and motivate you?

This could be.

- Mentors
- Coaches
- New social networks
- Influencers

Once you have identified your social circle of support and you have your team and support system in place, now you can start tackling the causes of the stressors at work that are keeping you in burnout.

It is important to also get professional medical advice on how burnout symptoms are affecting your mental and physical health and to establish if there are any other matters in your life that may be contributing to how you are feeling. That is what we will look at in chapter nine.

Burn-Brighter step:

1. Take a piece of paper or find the page in your workbook and create three columns. In the first, write down all the people you are connected with in the following areas:
   1. Family
   2. Friends
   3. Work associates
   4. Community

Write down everybody you are connected to, whether you get along with them or not, just everyone you have contact with or who influences your life in any way. You could use this list to create your own social map – and really look at how much energy you are putting into nurturing your relationships with family and friends. Remember, if you want to have a friend you have to be a friend.

As well as our close relationships, we all have wider connections with people across the different circles of our lives – at work, in our communities, or through our social activities. Although these relationships are less deep, these are also important for happiness and well-being. Add to Column 1 any others you might not have thought about before now, like a teacher from your schooldays, or a work colleague, or family member who was particularly influential.

What about a TV personality, author, or politician? Has a musician, playwright or artist influenced you?

Write them all down in Column 1.

In Column 2 you look at how this network could help you become more resilient. In the second column of your list, note how each person influences your life (Good or Bad?) and what you can learn from them.

Think about how they affected you and your belief systems. Were they a positive influence and inspired you, or did they put you down, or upset you, and make you feel bad about yourself? Did they push you forwards towards success, or hold you back?

In the third column, think about how you can make changes to those network connections for your benefit. If the person is a good influence or is supportive and brings positive things to your life, you may want to make more time for them or get in touch if you haven't done so for a while. You could try 21 days of gratitude – and on each day write an email or letter to someone you are grateful for. This will create ripples of positivity that will light up your social circle.

If someone on your list does not feel so healthy for you, you might wish to see less of them, or break that connection. If it is someone from the past who has influenced you, think about whether you wish to continue allowing them to do so.

Now this exercise is quite deep so please be gentle with yourself. If it throws up something for you that is emotionally challenging, give yourself time and space to reflect on that and get some support if you need it. This exercise can then be repeated once you have had time to reflect on the shifts in your energy levels after making any changes.

Well done for getting this far. This looks simple but can be really challenging work and often something we do not want to go really deep into. Now we'll look at who can help you start your recovery journey.

Chapter 9

How To Get Help Part 2: The Professionals

Sometimes, even a strong social circle isn't enough to combat burnout. In these cases, who could you go to for help? Here are a few suggestions that we will look at in a bit more detail in this chapter.

- Doctor
- Occupational health
- Psychologist
- Counsellor
- Holistic/alternative therapist

Before you speak to a medical professional:

- Have you made a note of how you are feeling and any stressful events or experiences that may have contributed to this?

- It is also a good idea to make a note of how this is affecting your work and daily life.
- How is your mental and physical health being affected?

Seeing your doctor

It's all too easy to self-diagnose using online sites or advice from friends and family, but there is no substitute for seeing a qualified medical professional to get a diagnosis. This can provide reassurance and something to work on through recovery, but it also has a practical benefit: if you are going to take time out of your work, an official diagnosis may be needed to ensure that you get any sick pay you are contracted to receive. A letter from a doctor may be the ticket you need to trigger your workplace sickness absence and rehabilitation processes.

For those who are self-employed or in the 'gig economy' this might not be available, and the fear of taking time out to heal can add to the pressure to keep going. If you don't work, you don't earn. Depending on where you live, there may be welfare benefits available or support, but usually these are only available if you have been given a diagnosis by a doctor, so it is important to get advice and support to help you to access them.

This is also where income protection benefits could help. Have you been paying into policies for years and never thought when you might need them? Now might be the time.

The most important thing to help you recover is to get recognition that you are experiencing burnout so you can start working with your employer (and that includes yourself if you are your own boss) to make changes to reduce your exposure to toxic stress.

When you go to your doctor, make sure you note how you have been feeling, the factors that have contributed to them, and the impact it is having on your daily life. It can help to write this down, especially if you are experiencing low-mood, low-energy levels. The reflection tools in this book could help you make a list of prompts to help in the often time-pressured environment of the consulting room.

You may be asked to complete a wellbeing measuring tool to identify if you are experiencing depression, and your doctor may also check for other issues that could be causing low mood or low energy. It is important to be honest and share everything that is going on for you, both at work and at home so you can really see all the factors that are contributing to how you are feeling.

If you are struggling to get an appointment with your doctor, don't give up. There are other professionals who can help.

Occupational Health

Occupational health professionals look at the effects of work on health and of health on ability to do work. If you are experiencing symptoms of burnout, now is the time to get in touch with them.

Your employer may have an occupational-health team or outsourced employee support programme that provides a confidential phone support service. They could also offer access to medical professionals to help you with a diagnosis and psychological assessment and support. Depending how your employer contracts in the service, they could be independent or part of the Human resources team (HR) or other employee management function of the organisation, and although they should be bound by confidentiality, it is important for you to know what their reporting line is and what their influence is in terms of implementing any recommendations to support you in reducing exposure to any identified workplace stressors. Key to developing trust is how your records are managed and how they interact with your management when reviewing your working arrangements and stress risk assessments.

Talking therapies

It's good to talk; yet many of us don't feel able to share our worries, frustrations, or reflections about the things that are bothering us. We allow our 'inner committee' of self-critics and imposter syndrome to process things instead. This can turn into rumination and dwelling on situations or actions that have upset us or have caused us to feel stressed. It can seem like there is no escape from our anxieties if the 'negative Nelly' and imposter syndrome/critic members of the committee are allowed to speak loudest.

Talking to family and friends about stressful situations, and your concerns or worries can sometimes be all you need to get a new perspective on a situation, or realise it is not worth spending your time and energy on it any longer. However, for the bigger stuff, or the things that we are feeling guilt, shame or fear about, this may not be an option and it could be better to talk to a professional therapist who can support you.

It is important here to remember that you first may need to see a medical professional to check if you are experiencing any mental-health conditions so that they can be treated first as going into any type of talking therapy may make the condition worse, or affect your treatment.

Any therapist who takes on a client should ask if you are receiving treatment for a mental health condition and should discuss with you how their therapy may (or may not) be compatible with the treatment you are receiving for it.

It is also important to remember that although talking therapies have been the standard referral route for people experiencing low-level mental-health conditions such as anxiety and depression for many years, where trauma is involved, experts are now realising that this may not be the best option for all, as some treatments can re-traumatise us and actually do us more harm.

Trauma expert Professor Bessel van der Volk has suggested that focusing on talk therapy might not be the most effective route in all cases to treating trauma, as it can be painful to talk about. Some people may have difficulty finding the words to describe their experiences as they trigger a strong emotional response. The brain can't distinguish between past and present when setting off the stress response to the trigger.

He goes on to point out that *'Even if a patient does feel comfortable sharing their trauma story, this doesn't always*

mean that talking progresses treatment. While it may pro-
vide comfort or help make sense of a horrific event, it might
also cause a patient to stagnate in their healing'. (Van der
Kolk)

and,

"At some point, the story often becomes an alibi. For many
traumatised people, they tell the same story over and over
again. Instead of feeling things very deeply, they go through a
recital of misery, which is not the same thing as psychother-
apy." (Van der Kolk)
– Bessel van der Kolk, MD.

Let's look at the types of talking therapists you may want
to see. As with any type of professional service, it is important
to check the accreditation of any practitioner if you are seeking
private services outside of your national health service providers
which can often have long wait times for referrals.

Psychologist

A psychologist is a professional trained in how the mind
works. They are able to help patients solve problems that are
affecting their mental health. They are not required to be medi-
cally qualified, so can't diagnose anything that is not related to
your mental state. Due to that, it is important to see a doctor
first to identify any physical health issues that you could be
experiencing as a result of or contributing to your burnout

such as menopause, diabetes or a post-viral fatigue issue like long covid.

It took me decades to get around to see a psychologist as none of the doctors or counsellors I saw in the times I had experienced breakdowns or depression had made a referral. Once I did – and got a diagnosis of PTSD – it felt like a release in some ways to realise that my repeated episodes of depression and low mood and the coping strategies I had put in place to protect me from harm were a result of my past trauma. Over time, I processed the explanations that my psychologist had given me about these coping strategies and I understood more about how these traumas were keeping me stuck in the burnout cycle.

I learned that I was constantly on alert (hypervigilance) and avoiding conflict (people pleasing) at the expense of meeting my own needs and preserving my energy by setting and protecting boundaries on my time.

However, my experience of seeing a psychologist was only the beginning of my recovery journey. It was just one appointment, an hour long, to talk through what was affecting my mood and to talk about past experiences. It was, on reflection, re-traumatising, as I talked to them I effectively re-experienced the stress response that I had learned in response to the events that had traumatised me in the past, and was shown how they had affected my mental state in the present.

Be prepared – being told these new 'truths' can also be traumatising, and trigger a whole raft of emotions like anger, shame, guilt, and fear about how many years of your life have been wasted on living with the impacts that the traumatising events have had on your life.

So how does this actually help you beat burnout?

Just keep in mind that one meeting is the beginning of a process, not the process itself. A psychologist could help you identify the causes of your burnout, so you can really see what you need to work on instead of hiding from it. However, it is likely that you may need additional support to work through the impacts, beliefs, and behaviours that you have developed in response to them. This help could be in the form of a counsellor or other type of therapist.

Counsellor

There are many types of counsellor and this book isn't going to be able to describe all of them so this is just a brief description on what a counsellor could help you with and how you might find one.

Counselling, also described as a type of 'talking therapy,' is primarily focussed on past experiences and how they affect your emotional state in the *present*. It can help you find reasons why you think and behave the way you do, and how you respond to your stress triggers and to people in your life, including yourself.

Counselling can take many forms, but generally consists of talking to a qualified therapist about your past experiences and reflecting on how they made you feel. It can help to uncover hidden root causes of present behaviours and stress responses, with someone who will listen to you and support you without judgement.

Counselling can take place in person, on the phone, or online – using conferencing software, apps, or by email. You should be able to access this type of support relatively easily from anywhere in the world.

Counselling can help you gain a better understanding of your feelings and thought processes, and identify your own possible ways to resolve problems, but the counsellor will not usually give advice or tell you what to do. That, not surprisingly , is the role of a coach, whose role is to work with you on _present_ and _future_ challenges, and not deal with the past. However, to have an effective coaching experience, it would be better to have dealt with any past trauma so that you are more open to working on mindset issues with your coach.

Talk therapy can be effective in some situations as for some people, sharing a past traumatic experience can be empowering – particularly if they've kept the trauma a secret for years. But in order to truly release the stored trauma from your body, you will need to use additional or alternative ways, which is what we will look at next.

Holistic and Alternative Therapies

'The mind and body are actually different sides of the same coin
that goes all the way back to the origins of medicine. For most
of its history, the practice was not separated from other aspects
of human activity.'
—Jon Kabatt-Zinn

When *The Body Bears the Burden* was published by Robert Scaer in 2001 (Scaer), it changed the way people thought about trauma, PTSD, and the treatment of chronic stress disorders. Now the book is in its third edition and Scaer shares more examples of clinicians' explorations of the connections between mind, brain, and body, as well as the many and varied ways that we can notice symptoms of traumatic stress and burnout.

Cutting-edge trauma research is building the evidence that body-based interventions are necessary for lasting healing and recovery. The terms 'complementary' and 'alternative' are often used to describe these treatments and the differences between these two terms have been defined by the US National Center for Complementary and Integrative Health (NCCIH) like this:

- When a non-mainstream practice is used together with conventional medicine, it's considered "complementary".
- When a non-mainstream practice is used *instead of* conventional medicine, it's considered "alternative".

Of course, there can be overlap between these classifications for example, aromatherapy may sometimes be used as a complementary treatment to aid relaxation whilst undergoing the conventional treatment, whereas in other circumstances is used as an alternative to conventional treatment.

A number of complementary and alternative treatments can be effective in dealing with the physical and mental-health symptoms of burnout. There are many different types of therapies, so I'm not going to go into details of every one here but share a few that I've found helpful in my recovery journey.

Holistic therapeutic approaches may include but are not limited to: acupuncture, acupressure, biofeedback, massage therapy, chiropractic, manual therapy, naturopathic medicine, meditation and guided imagery, yoga, therapeutic touch, reiki and other energy therapies including emotional freedom techniques (EFT).

Meditation

"Half an hour's meditation each day is essential, except when you are busy. Then a full hour is needed."
— Saint Francis de Sales

I love this quote as it describes beautifully how meditation can quite literally 'bend time' as the more you meditate, the less 'busy' you become – yet you still get more done!

If done regularly, meditation can be one of the most powerful tools in your resilience toolkit, as it can not only help you stay calm and focused – it can actually *grow* the parts of your brain required for compassion, empathy, problem solving, and creativity, and *shrink* the amygdala and related stress response circuits – imaging if there was a magic pill for that?

And you can access this for *free* in just a few minutes every day!

Why do we not teach this as part of school curriculums across the board?

Imagine how different our schools could be?

My meditation journey began when I was in therapy after my last big burnout episode. It was a perfect storm of trauma, grief, stress, and confusion, mixed in with heaps of fear, anger, anxiety, and frustration. I had no idea how to even start unravelling all those emotions and thoughts going through my head! I got signed off work with depression and was sent to a course of cognitive behavioural therapy (CBT, see next section). The therapist introduced me to the work of Jon Kabat-Zinn, in the form of his book (co-authored with Williams, Teasdale, and Segal - Guildford), *The Mindful Way Through Depression: Freeing Yourself from Chronic Unhappiness*. (Zinn et al.)

If you haven't come across Jon's life-changing teachings, I'd highly recommend them. He is renowned internationally for his work as a scientist, writer, and meditation teacher and can be credited as a main player in bringing mindfulness into the mainstream of medicine and society.

This book was a complete revelation to me, and for the first time in my life I began to explore meditation and allowing myself to just *be* and be still. Admittedly it was not for very long at first as my mind was still hypervigilant and on auto-pilot self-critical mode as this was all that I knew at that time.

But as I worked through the eight-week mindfulness-based stress-reduction course (MBSR) and tried all the guided meditations and yoga sequences they used, I started to notice a difference.

I felt calmer, and for the first time in forty years, I had experienced a feeling of safety. It felt so nice! And the best bit was that I could do this anywhere and at any time I wanted to.

In the past decade I have tried all sorts of different types of meditation, and the beauty of having technology at our fingertips is that you can easily access meditation apps and teachers on your computer or phone. There are lots of great books containing teachings and 'how to meditate' lessons, and many thousands of teachers and classes available to access in person and online.

I would recommend trying a few different types of meditation to see what feels right for you. Even if you just take five minutes out of your day in the morning and evening to sit calm and meditate using whatever method you choose, I promise you it will make a difference.

It might also help for you to write down what comes up for you during or after each meditation session. It may help to go back to the acceptance and reflection steps in this book. It is sometimes when we allow our minds to be still that the real insights are allowed to surface. In this state, we can connect with how we truly feel about situations that may be being masked by our busyness and fight/flight/freeze stress response that we get stuck in when we burnout. If you are not a person who likes to journal (which could be seen as a form of reflective meditation in itself), a simple bullet list in a dedicated notebook would work just as well to clear those thoughts from your mind onto the page.

What meditation trains us to do is to open our minds and allow what is already here to come in and be seen (Acceptance) without judgement and then allow the thoughts that fill our minds to pass by without responding to them. This skill becomes more developed as you practise more. Like I described in Chapter 5, when you respond to a thought, it causes a signal to fire in that neural pathway, so put in its simplest terms, if we stop strengthening those pathways, we can remodel them in other ways through meditation.

I'm not going to even begin to go into the many forms of meditation that you could try – that would be a whole new book in itself! (Great idea for my second book maybe?).

Instead I'll share a few simple introductory exercises you can use to see how simple and accessible meditation can be, and bust the myth that it is long periods of time sitting cross-legged on a yoga mat chanting and burning incense (although that is one way of doing it!).

Burn-Brighter Step:

1. Try this simple breathing meditation - you can download the FREE audio guidance here (https://bit.ly/Beatburnoutmeditationaudio)
2. Start your day with a three minute mini-meditation:
    1. Set your timer and spend one minute tuning into awareness of your thoughts, feelings, and body sensations;

    2. Now spend one minute of focused attention on breathing; breathe in for a count of four, lower your chin and hold for four, then raise your chin and let go of the breath for a count

of four. Repeat for the minute and notice how you feel afterwards.

3. Finally spend one minute scanning up through your body as a whole. Starting with the feet (and remembering to breathe!) focus on each area working up to the head and noting any tension, aches or pains as you go and with each breath out, allow each part to relax.

You could also set reminders to do this throughout the day – an easy three minutes to keep you calm and focussed. Got to be in your toolkit, right?

I'll leave this section with this quote from Thich Nhat Hanh, a spiritual leader, poet, and peace activist:

"Meditation can help us embrace our worries, our fear, our anger; and that is very healing. We let our own natural capacity of healing do the work."

Emotional Freedom Technique (EFT)

EFT has been shown to be a highly effective evidence-based somatic intervention for a whole range of emotional, physical and trauma related issues (Church et al.).

Emotional Freedom Technique (EFT) is a practical mind-body therapy that combines gentle tapping on acupressure meridian points with repeating mindful and intentional phrases. This can help release limiting beliefs or memories that may be causing anxiety, lack of confidence or emotional responses to a variety of situations. Energy is released and the client can tune into the core issues that they can then process or release and reduce the fight/flight response to the original trigger.

For many years, this technique was not viewed as a recognised therapeutic treatment but many practitioners and researchers gathered evidence on its effectiveness. In 2012 Psychologist David Feinstein conducted a meta-analysis of the energy psychology efficacy literature, and that changed the American Psychological Association (APA) view on this technique.

Energy Psychology research indicates that meridian-based interventions are at least as good as conventional therapeutic treatments, if not better, at relieving particularly post-traumatic stress, anxiety and other stresses, as well as their related issues such as phobias, David's article convinced the APA, and his work helped EFT attain what is the highest level of proof in the treatment of mental health: 'probably efficacious'.

Top-level medical doctors specialising in trauma, like Dr Robert Scaer ('Body Bears the Burden,' 'Trauma Spectrum' and www.traumasoma.com), and people researching and theorising about psychological recovery from trauma like Dr Stephen Porges ('PolyVagal Nerve Theory') and Peter Levine ('Waking the Tiger'), all recommend acupressure point stimulation that is used in EFT to relieve psychological stress, and Dr Gordon Turnbull, author of 'Trauma' (Turnbull #), who has worked with special forces and countless other military personnel, talks about EFT as a promising field of treatment.

But how does EFT work? Well, as we have evolved from the days of living in a cave, our natural defence mechanisms that protect us from danger have not changed, and our brain still releases the same chemical triggers to prepare our bodies for fight or flight – whether we are being chased by a tiger or paying expensive bills. We may not be running from predators, but we are still triggered in other ways in our busy lives. If we don't find healthy ways to release these chemicals, they can have harmful physical and mental-health effects over our lifetime.

You may have memories or experiences in your past that have been stored or repressed to prevent you from experiencing the trauma again, and this sometimes manifests itself in protective or destructive behaviours that can affect your work and personal life, limiting what you could possibly do or holding you back from reaching your full potential. EFT tapping can help release those stored memories and allow you to live a freer life again.

There have been many studies on the benefits of EFT. Scientific studies using brain scans by Harvard medical school have shown that stimulation of meridian acupressure points can significantly decrease activity of the Amygdala, hippocampus and other fear-associated parts of the brain (go back to Chapter 2 to remind yourself about how they work).

Studies involving measurements of blood chemical markers for stress including cortisol and adrenaline have also shown the positive effect of tapping, with a significant drop in levels of both hormones after just one hour of tapping, and measurable improvements in psychological symptoms in the participants.

Many more studies on energy psychology techniques have been published showing EFT tapping to be extremely effective in reducing or even eliminating PTSD symptoms in a range of settings including war veterans and survivors of genocide in Rwanda. In 2018, NICE officially recommended EFT as worthy of government research funds for treating trauma and PTSD. (all articles described above are cited here https://eftinternational.org/nice-recommendations-for-eft/)

There are some fantastic resources detailing how to tap available online. Dr Peta Stapleton has written an excellent book explaining the science behind tapping (Stapleton) which complements her excellent TEDex talk on 'Is Therapy Facing a Revolution?' (Stapleton) where she explains why EFT is fast becoming recognised as part of the fourth wave of therapy.

My EFT Story

This is my story of how EFT helped me break free from burnout and recover from PTSD.

I was diagnosed with complex PTSD when I was 38, after suffering multiple bouts of depression throughout my early 20s and 30s. My mother had alcohol dependency and was a mental-health service user who took out her mood swings on me. I had years of mental and physical abuse which culminated in her being sectioned for a violent incident aimed at me. After I left education, I experienced bullying at work as I was unable to maintain healthy boundaries due to my previous traumas.

I had classic complex PTSD symptoms – avoidance of conflict, perfectionism, high expectations of self and others –

leading to frequent burnout, stress, self-criticism, and exhaustion. The clinical psychologist complimented me on my resources and coping strategies in dealing with the trauma for so long, and shared some tools with me that I could use to face my fears to allow images and thoughts about the past to play through my mind and lose their potency. Until I discovered EFT, I had not found a way to do that without causing me more trauma.

I left home at 17 (kicked out after getting caught up in a domestic incident), and only escaped the dysfunctional family situation by moving in with a relative so I could complete my education to get to university. After training as a scientist, I ended up in a professional Health and Safety role.

I now realise that I moved into a career in Health and Safety to keep people safe because I didn't ever feel safe myself. My identity centred around keeping people safe. I became incredibly stressed and never switched off.

I tried counselling and Cognitive Behavioural therapy, as well as training as a mental health first aider and finding ways to reduce the shame and stigma I felt about my mental health. Art helped me to find some calm. I also tried exercise including training for two marathons. However, a further stressful period in my life led me to try EFT for the first time.

Our young family was forced to relocate over 500 miles to care for my mother-in-law who had just received a life-changing diagnosis of an aggressive, incurable brain cancer. We were all quite traumatised by the move, grieving for our home, the impact of her diagnosis, and adjusting to the caring responsibilities as well as settling our kids into a new school and new workplaces. We had nine months of this exhausting and stressful plate-spinning, made worse by the sadness and trauma of watching a loved one fade away. The shock of her passing was soon followed eight months later by the grief and the additional shock of my father-in-law passing.

We moved again, this time into our in-laws house to clear and renovate it, and were then faced with legal threats from family members over probate relating to the house. On top of the double grief my family were feeling, we now had the additional stress of the lawyers' letters (and accompanying bills) landing through the post-box as we were working through dealing with all of the many possessions that our late mother and father-in-law had hoarded over seventy years. I became so low during this time, exhausted and feeling isolated and anxious about where we might live, and this triggered memories of being kicked out of home as a teenager.

I also had a lot of anger and financial worries as I had given up a good salary and pension to relocate to care for my in-laws and was only able to work part time because of my caring responsibilities, so we couldn't get a mortgage.

My friend was training as an EFT practitioner and needed case study volunteers, so I jumped at the chance. I was desperate to try anything that might help me find a solution to our housing and other emotional challenges.

So, in January 2018, I went (with a little apprehension I must admit) to my first EFT tapping session, with the intention of helping my friend out and curiosity to see what might emerge.

In the first session we started tapping on the current issues around our family challenges and recent bereavements. This felt strange at first, but the practitioner was skilled at making me feel safe. In that first hour, I felt calmer, even while talking about the stressful situation I was in. I was able to explore my feelings around them in a way that I had never been able to before. Before then, talking would have triggered and re-traumatised me, but now, I could talk with ease.

I had tried talking and cognitive behavioural therapies years before, and had been practising mindfulness and meditation for a number of years, so I had a good understanding of how our thoughts can affect our physical state and how to be present with my emotions.

The act of tapping while talking really calmed down my emotional response to the things that were coming up in my mind as the session developed.

I shed a lot of tears during that first session and yawned a lot too. Both are quite common indicators that the tapping is working. The practitioner explained that these responses helped to release the energy blocks and emotions trapped in my body from the years of chronic stress and trauma response.

I felt quite exhausted, but so much lighter after the first session, and spent the week between that and the next session noting down all sorts of things that were bubbling up from my mind that I hadn't allowed myself to notice before.

In the second and third session I felt more comfortable working through some really deep core emotional traumas relating to my adverse childhood experiences that had left me feeling anxious and hypervigilant, and thus more vulnerable to stress as an adult ("Hypervigilance and PTSD – PTSD UK"). One of the key coping mechanisms the PTSD sufferers often have is avoidance of conflict. As I was deeply involved in a family conflict at the time, this was really difficult for me to deal with. It was triggering my stress response every day.

We tapped on feeling loved, looked at my inner child and did some deep healing work to let go of the unloved child and reconnect with my adult self and then work on my anxieties, anger, and guilt about the challenges we were facing about our family situation. I also realised that my career in Health and Safety that had been causing me so much stress was part of the problem. I was trying to keep others safe because I never felt safe myself.

I walked out of the third session feeling even lighter and went straight to the estate agents to look for a house and booked some viewings, buoyed by the release of emotional pressure to find a secure home. Within five months of that session we had moved into our dream home and let go of the family legal challenges we had been subjected to.

I realised then how powerful this technique was, so I learned as much as I could about it. I continued to tap regularly, working through lists of issues. Through tapping, I peeled away years of trauma I had bottled up as I had been too scared or traumatised to look at them clearly. Now, I was not only looking at them but healing them.

I then decided to train as a practitioner so I could help others benefit from tapping. In the four years since my first EFT session, I have qualified as an advanced accredited EFT practitioner. Most crucially, I am no longer dominated by symptoms of PTSD, and when I notice any arising, I can tap on them and process them immediately.

I have also moved on to retrain in the creative career I always wanted to do but felt too scared to try. Before, I always felt I should stick with keeping myself and others safe. However, now, I am doing the work of my dreams. My job now brings me joy. EFT also has allowed me to start many more conversations about PTSD and mental health without fear of being triggered by the conversations I am having. I have even taken EFT tapping into schools to help pupils and teachers start to connect with their emotions in a safe (and fun) way. I have helped lots of people with my talks about EFT, both with single clients and in group coaching work.

I am much happier now as I choose who I want to work with and when I want to work. I have made it my mission to smash the stigma about talking about PTSD and have started the creating resilience podcast to help others share their stories of how creativity has made them more resilient. I would never have been able to do this without having EFT in my life and for that I am eternally grateful.

Would you like to try this fantastic tool? The basic process for tapping is shared below, and in the additional resources section you can learn how to set up your own 'personal peace procedure'.

However, I strongly recommend that for exploring more deeply held emotional challenges that you contact a qualified EFT practitioner. With a professional to guide you, you can be supported as you learn how to use this powerful technique. Uncovering any strong core emotional responses may require professional support to prevent a serious emotional reaction or disassociation, both of which could be harmful if not managed properly.

You can find a list of accredited EFT practitioners and a whole heap of resources on the EFT international website, https://eftinternational.org/ (you'll find me there too). Or, you can contact me direct at CreativeLeaderEFT@gmail.com

How to Tap

1. Decide on your Most Pressing Issue (MPI), i.e. what is causing you the most concern right now. For example, it could be that you feel angry about your work and how it is affecting you.

2. Rate the intensity of your emotional response to this issue (We call this the Subjective Unit of Distress SUD) on a scale of 1–10 where 1 is not bothered at all, and 10 is unbearable. Think about where in your body you feel it, does it have a colour, a strength, a texture? For example, if you think about something that angers you, you might feel a tightness in the

chest, or in your throat. It helps to really tune into this before you start tapping.

3. Think of a Setup Statement: for example *Even though I feel* _____ (e.g. 'Angry about feeling burned out'), *I deeply and completely* (this could be love/accept/forgive/trust myself).

   If that is too difficult right now as you are not yet able to believe that you accept/forgive/trust yourself, you could try saying 'honour how I feel' instead. The important thing is to say something that feels true for you right now as you are simply accepting whatever you are feeling without any judgement and the tapping will help you tune down the intensity of the emotional response until you feel safe to clear it, so say whatever feels right for you, not what you think you 'should' be saying.

4. Close your eyes, repeat the setup statement and feel where the issue is showing up in your body. It could be showing up as tension in your chest, shoulders, or throat for example.

5. Repeat the setup statement three times whilst tapping gently on the side of the hand point with your fingers (as many as you feel comfortable with, I use 1 or 2). So using the example above it could be: *Even though I feel Angry about feeling burned out, I deeply and completely accept myself and honour how I feel.*

6. Continue tapping round the following points:

a. Eyebrow: repeat the reminder phrase: e.g., 'this anger' whilst tapping gently with one or two fingers in between your eyebrows.

b. Side of eye: Say your reminder phrase and where you are feeling the emotion. e.g. *'I feel it in my shoulders'* whilst tapping gently on the side of your eye with two fingers. It doesn't matter which side you choose, and you could also use both hands and tap on both sides of your face.

c. Under eye: Repeat the reminder phrase: e.g. 'this anger....' whilst tapping gently on the bony bit just under your eye (again you can use one hand or both for this)

d. Under nose: Say a reminder phrase to connect with the *feeling*: e.g. ' *these feelings of anger'* whilst tapping on space between the upper lip and the nose.

e. Chin: State reminder phrase around the physical sensation of the feeling: e.g. *'this tension in my shoulders.....'* whilst tapping gently on the chin just under the bottom lip.

f. Collarbone: Say a reminder phrase about how it feels (intensity, temperature etc): e.g. *'it feels so tight......'* whilst tapping gently on the point a few fingers' width either side of where your collar bones meet, if you use two hands for this you can get really playful with this and release your inner gorilla. Kids love this point!

g. Under arm: Say a reminder phrase to talk about the feelings as thoughts: e.g., *'these angry thoughts they won't go away'* as you tap gently under your arm (around the point where the bra-line is ladies). If you use two hands for this point you can give yourself a lovely hug whilst tapping.

h. Now go to the top of your head, with your whole hand gently tapping with all your fingers around your head.

i. You've now completed a round of tapping!

j. This can be repeated as issues come up and to release, let go or reframe aspects that feel appropriate at the time

k. We normally end on a positive round of tapping to answer the most pressing issue that was in the setup statement. For example *'Even though I was feeling angry about feeling burned out, I am choosing to release these feelings and find healthier ways of dealing with my work.'*

And end again tapping on the top of the head.

7. Take a *deep* breath and release any remaining tension.

8. **Focus** into your body again and notice what's happening now. Did the issue shift? Quite often you can 'chase the pain' as you tune into and release the tension or strong physical sensations. They are released as you consciously relax those areas, and they move around your body until you no longer feel the need

to hold onto the emotion that was causing the physical response.

9. Where do you feel anything now?
10. What thoughts came up while tapping? Any 'yes but such as

   I have to hold onto this anger as if I don't stay angry it makes it OK what has happened.

11. Measure how you feel now about the original statement: rate the intensity (SUD) 1–10

NOTE: Again, you may uncover thoughts or feelings that require professional support to process, so it is important to make sure that you get the right support from an accredited EFT practitioner or medical professional depending on what comes up for you. You can contact Ann at CreativeLeaderEFT@gmail.com for advice.

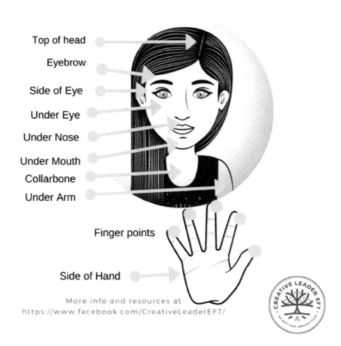

BE KIND TO YOUR MIND

EFT Tapping for beginners: Tapping points

Top of head
Eyebrow
Side of Eye
Under Eye
Under Nose
Under Mouth
Collarbone
Under Arm

Finger points

Side of Hand

More info and resources at
https://www.facebook.com/CreativeLeaderEFT/

What can you do with the 'yes buts' that come up when you are tapping? Well you can carry on tapping on each one as they come up until you have peeled away the layers to get to the core issue that you may not have been able to handle until you cleared the emotional intensity of the protective behaviours and thoughts around it, or you could list the issues that came up and create a 'personal peace procedure' which is simply a list of things you might like to process using EFT tapping.

Here is a short guide on how to do it. Can you list the top twenty most stressful issues with your work, family, health, or spiritual life right now? What is keeping you from moving out of the 'Fear Zone' into your greatest self?

Please note: this process is not intended to replace treatment by a qualified medical or other practitioner so if there is something on your list that is causing you emotional distress and could re-traumatise you without specialist support, you are advised to contact your GP or other relevant qualified medical professional

Burn-Brighter Step:

Create your own 'personal peace procedure'.

Take a blank page and divide it into three columns:

- In Column 1 just write the first thing that comes into your head. (For example, 'My work is stressful', 'I'm scared of public speaking', 'I still haven't finished that work project' etc. etc.)
- Then in Column 2 rate each issue by how much it bothers you (1 = not at all, 10 = unbearable).
- In Column 3 decide if you can let go of worrying about this issue, or need to take action to deal with how you respond to it – either by getting support or by working on your thoughts and feelings about the issue.

Chapter 10
Turn the Tables on Burnout

"Never forget: This very moment, we can change our lives.
There never was a moment, and never will be, when we are
without the power to alter our destiny."
—Stephen Pressfield

It's OK to not be OK.

I hope that this book so far has helped you realise that burnout is not an individual weakness, but a response to experiencing chronic workplace and other stresses, and you may be more vulnerable to burning out if you have experienced trauma or other developmental, attachment or discrimination challenges in your life .

What I want to show you in the last chapter of this book is that we can create new habits and use lots of different tools to raise your energy levels, create healthy boundaries to protect them, and raise your levels of happiness.

In previous chapters you have learned what burnout is, how it can happen, and the significant costs it can have on your physical and mental health and pretty much all aspects of your life.

In the last chapter, we explored how, once you have recognised that you are burning out, you can get help and support to start breaking free. You can recover by recognising the beliefs, behaviours, and emotional responses that are keeping you trapped in the burnout cycle and responding to the toxic stress you are being exposed to at work.

So now, you have to work on building your own resilience toolkit, a toolkit that will enable you to whip the legs from under those tabletops of beliefs that have kept you stuck.

Let's start turning the tables towards more empowering and sustainable beliefs that can help you put in place healthy and strongly held boundaries on your time and energy. If you can do that, you can achieve a more balanced and fulfilled life where all of your needs are met.

This chapter will show you a selection of tools and strategies to help you.

Build your own resilience toolkit.

As nobody is sadly going to live a life free from stress, trauma, or suffering in any way, we have to find ways of becoming resilient and allowing ourselves to recover when these things do happen. If you have recognised that you are experiencing burnout and you are ready to recover, this chapter's tools can help you break free from burnout for good.

To get the most out of this section, I invite you to:

- Be curious.
- Think about how you could rewrite your beliefs about yourself and how you work.
- Be open to (re)connecting with activities that energise you.

Play More!

> *"Play is a holistic experience in that it invites our total being into the process".*
> —C.E. Schaffer

I had to get this in first as it is the first thing we lose as we transition from childhood into our adult selves. Play is often seen as childish – quite literally 'child's play', so it's no wonder that adults don't let themself play!

Do you remember when you were younger how much energy you had for playtime?

When did you last try making something, judgement-free, or play with different materials you haven't used before? When was the last time you allowed yourself to just go with the flow and not make a plan or try to control the outcome?

Play therapy is often used with children to support emotional health and process trauma, and is defined by the Association for Play Therapy (APT) as

> *"the systematic use of a theoretical model to establish an interpersonal process wherein trained play therapists use the therapeutic powers of play to*

help clients prevent or resolve psychosocial difficulties and achieve optimal growth and development"
("Association for Play Therapy (APT)").

Or put more simply– it's a form of therapy where clients play during the session with a range of materials and toys to express themselves and feel calm instead of just answering direct questions from the therapist. Although it is used mostly on children, this can be helpful for adults too as it can enable us to explore social connections, family roles, and emotional responses to past experiences.

As an artist and performer, I have had some profoundly healing and energising experiences in sessions where I have allowed myself to be playful and not worry about looking 'stupid' or childish. It felt so liberating to give myself permission to play with complete freedom. I have to note that I didn't start playing music or performing until I was in my 40s as the beliefs that were imprinted in me as a teen from my caregivers was that I was 'making a racket' when I tried to practise my instrument at home between school music lessons.

In contrast, I really miss those precious moments when I joined in with my own children's playtime. Anyone who has experienced the joy and energy of participating in a fully immersive play session with a young child – who has not yet encountered the societal pressures to 'act their age,' which often stifles the playfulness that nourished our younger selves – can relate.

In the next few sections, we will look at more healthy ways to start accepting yourself, dropping shame and guilt, and being more present so that you can work out better ways to deal with the root causes of the stresses that are causing you to burn out. By doing so, you can give yourself permission to play more without any fear of judgement from your own inner-critic or anyone else.

Get Creative

> *"Creativity is as important as literacy"*
> —Ken Robinson

Do I need to say more??

Researchers from the University of Otago have found that people report being happy and energised when they take part in creative activities, and this quote from the lead researcher sums it up nicely:

> *'Doing creative things today predicts improvements in well-being tomorrow. Full stop."*
> —Tamlin Conner, researcher, University of Otago
> in New Zealand

My own journey to breaking free from burnout through creativity was sparked by helping out an elderly neighbour. She was no longer able to drive due to her deteriorating eyesight caused by diabetes.

I met her at our local library where the art club was putting on a taster session, allowing us to play with paints. In the midst of one of my worst periods of depression (caused by burning out after months of trying to cope with bullying at work and the impact of my recent PTSD diagnosis) I had a life-changing revelation.

I felt so low and paranoid at the time that I was unable to cope with even taking my kids to school. I was so worried that people were looking at me and judging me. But then, that life-changing hour of sitting in the library and focusing on applying brushstrokes to paper allowed my mind to calm and just *be* for the first time in my adult life.

No more racing thoughts about what anyone else may be thinking about me or worrying about my exhaustion that was blocking me from functioning and looking after my family. I was purely in the moment, fascinated by how the colours blended and changed as they soaked into the paper.

Now, I didn't create a masterpiece that day, but what I did do was begin a ten-year road to recovery and resetting boundaries as well as seeing the world in a completely different way.

Since starting this journey of enabling and developing my creativity, I have looked at everything through the lens of an artist, thinking, *how might I paint or draw that?* I have found peace in really noticing the colours of each sunset, cloud or flower with curiosity as I wonder how I might mix those on a canvas or draw them.

Engaging in creative activities of any sort requires you to interact with the materials of whatever medium you are using, and if you are a performer (dancing, music, acting, poetry) you are also interacting with your fellow performers and the audience too, forming a social connection. I'll share the benefits of that later in this chapter!

Arts Council England recently published its new Creative Health and Well-being strategy and in it they explain what creative health and well-being *is-*

> , ….." *the connection between creativity and the health and quality of people's lives. We believe that creative and cultural activity must be viewed by society as a fundamental part of living well* ' ("Creative Health & Wellbeing")

Their strategy for taking creativity into communities to support better wellbeing includes a workstream on how people can develop personal creativity at every stage of their lives.

I have lost count of the number of times people have told me 'I'm not creative.' People who say that view creativity as being able to achieve what is in their view a 'professional' standard in drawing , painting, music or whatever artform they are thinking of. What they don't see is how they cook and present food, how they arrange their homes, how they dress, select music, write, or plan projects – all of these everyday activities can include creativity as you are applying your unique spin on how they are presented. If we all dressed, ate, wrote the same and had identical homes, the world would be an extremely dull place!

As we discovered in Chapter 2, your amazing brain has a primitive safety mechanism at its core that shuts down non-essential functions when it is triggered by a perceived threat.

When you are experiencing what your mind thinks is something that needs your stress response, you will not be able to think creatively or logically.

By engaging fully and immersing yourself in a creative activity, you are by definition not in the stress response and your mind can rest in a flow state.

There is a whole bunch of neuroscience research evidence showing the brain state when engaged in a creative task. Turns out, brains that are thinking creatively look similar to brains that are meditating.

As an artist, poet, and performer I can vouch for the complete bliss of being totally immersed in the creative flow and not noticing anything else for hours if allowed to enjoy some precious creative play time.

Creativity also helps deal with one of the traits that can lead to burnout: fear of failure and of making mistakes.

This quote from abstract painter Agnes Martin sums up what true resilience means: the ability to fail and fail but still keep going with something that you are passionate about.

"There will be moving ahead and discoveries made every day. There will be great disappointments and failures in trying to express them. An artist is one who can fail and fail and still go on."

Agnes was trailblazer for female artists from the 1950s onwards and her work, influenced by Zen Buddhism and abstract minimalism, has been described by a critic as an "essay in discretion on inward-ness and silence". She lived with mental health challenges, but did not allow herself or her work to be defined by them.

I had the good fortune to be able to see some of her work up close on a visit to the Guggenheim museum in New York, and looking at the detailed grids she painstakingly applied to her canvases it is quite easy to see where this quote came from.

A series of talks organised by Healing Arts London in 2021 contained a wealth of evidence and case studies to show just how important creativity is for not only creating recovery, but promoting and maintaining positive mental and physical health too.

Backed by the WHO and a host of scientists, medical and creative practitioners these panel discussions and talks showed how artistic practices have been used in hospitals and schools, communities, and prisons, with all age groups and sections of society to promote community, reduce isolation and help communicate needs, emotions and ideas, to solve problems, increase engagement, and to just make people feel good!

There are too many examples to list here, but you can see the series of talks on their YouTube channel (Van Tulleken and Chatterjee). The first session has experts from the WHO, science, health and arts professions all talking passionately about the role that creativity has in wellbeing. The - 'Frame of Mind' discussion includes emotional testimony from Sir

Anthony Gormley and actor Gillian Anderson about the healing power of art.

The UK has set up a National Centre for Creative health, so we are moving towards a more "whole person whole life" approach to health and well-being. In the UK, our NHS healthcare providers and commissioning bodies are linking with networks of creative practitioners to deliver socially engaged creative therapeutic programmes: just imagine if workplace wellbeing programmes started thinking this way too? There is also a 'Prescribe Arts' network forming where doctors, patients and care coordinators can look up creative groups and activities like choirs, art groups, and theatre groups to signpost to that can support well-being.

Maybe your workplace could benefit from a corporate choir or creative writing or art group, where stressed executives were able to sing, play with clay, or sketch portraits to relax, instead of going to the pub after work.

Creating a path out of the burnout epidemic could be as easy as engaging an artist or other creative facilitator to help your people play more. This could give a significant return on investment in better productivity, team building and absence reduction…and it also could be fun!

Burn-Brighter Step:

- Think about what creative activities you enjoy (whether or not you actually do any of them right now).
- Now write down how much time you currently spend doing them.
- Does this feel like enough time for you to feel the benefits or get some balance in your life?
- How could you change this to support you more?

Embrace Acceptance and GREAT DREAMs

"My happiness grows in direct proportion to my acceptance, and in inverse proportion to my expectations."
—Michael J. Fox

It may seem odd that you should have to accept that you are feeling so low that you can't face your job, or even anything else if you have reached the point of complete exhaustion, but if you think about it, you are using vital energy denying, suppressing or being self-critical about the situation you are in when you're burnt out.

Try it next time you get mad at something or someone, or frustrated about something not happening. Just breathe and accept that whatever is happening is, indeed, happening. It won't make it right, whatever it is, but by accepting it, you are allowing some headspace and not triggering your stress response or 'victim mode'.

The late great Louise Hay coined a great phrase on this-

"If you want to clean house, you first have to see the dirt".

— Louise Hay

This is something that I have struggled with as it is so much easier to bury your feelings and not see the things that may be difficult to face up to.

So if you are unhappy in your job, or you are having money worries, or relationship difficulties, it is really important not to hide them and pretend they are not there as your mind does not forget and you will be using up more energy hiding than accepting these challenging issues.

The field of positive psychology is huge and there are many great teachers out there who can show you how to bring more joy and happiness into your life.

Have a GREAT DREAM approach.

I had the privilege of running a monthly group for the Action for Happiness network during the two-year period we were in COVID-19 lockdowns. Action for Happiness was founded by Lord Richard Layard, Geoff Mulgan and Sir Anthony Seldon and its patron is The Dalai Lama. They help people take action to improve mental well-being, both for themselves and others. The movement's vision is a happier and more caring society where people feel good, function well and help others. With over 100,000 members in 170 countries and an online community of over one million followers it provides evidence-based resources to help people, runs courses and training for communities, schools, and organisations; and promotes cultural change towards a more compassionate way of life. Their teachings and group work promote well-being and build community connection, and evaluation evidence from over 1,000 course attendees showing significant improvements in both their personal well-being, life satisfaction and pro-social behaviours such as compassion and trust.

This was such a wonderful experience for me, sharing a journey through the "*10 keys to happier living*" framework they teach based on the work of psychologist Vanessa King (King).

The "big questions" we explored together using the 'GREAT DREAM' framework developed by King in the 10 keys book (King) included:

1. What really matters in life?
2. What actually makes us happy?
3. Can we find peace of mind?
4. How should we treat others?
5. What makes for great relationships?
6. Can we be happier at work?
7. Can we build happier communities?
8. How can we create a happier world?

We explored them using a mixture of group discussion, individual reflection and meditation as well as learning from experts and each other. Then, we were tasked with creating an accountability culture by committing to taking one small action step to focus on before our next meeting. The optional action steps are the 10 keys (King #), and they included:

- Giving
- Relating
- Exercising
- Awareness
- Trying out
- Direction
- Resilience
- Emotions
- Acceptance
- Meaning

You can learn more about their work and the GREAT DREAM elements here www.actionforhappiness.org.

Burn-Brighter Step:

- What do you need to move towards accepting when it comes to your work or home life right now?
- What does 'happiness' look like for you?
- What does your life look like in each of the ten keys listed above?

Reflect and direct your own story.

*'Reflection is one of the most underused
yet powerful tools for success'*
—Richard Carlson

Reflective practice is an essential tool to have in your resilience toolkit. Consistent reflection gives you a chance to assess your life and how you have been spending your time, as well as prompting you to think about where you are now compared with where you had planned to or would like to be.

It also gives you a chance to really connect with your feelings about the events you are reflecting on, and an opportunity to work through any challenging emotions that may arise. Then, you can make changes to have different experiences moving forward. So if you were sharing with a friend how your day went yesterday, how might it sound?

I'm going to let you into a secret here – you have the power to choose how you tell your story. We humans have an inbuilt habit of focussing on what went wrong or *didn't* happen, and often forget about or play down all the amazing things we have experienced. So in your storytelling, make sure you take account of EVERYTHING, including the good stuff that you often overlook! Did you mention the people who were kind to you, or then you sailed through a green light or found that prized parking spot on your commute? Or the delicious food you had to eat, or the projects and work tasks you completed?

Another useful exercise to develop from this reflective storytelling is to hone down your experiences to descriptive themes, such as 'growth', 'learning', 'transformation', 'focus' etc. Try it for the last month's experiences and see if you can come up with a three-word summary. You can then reflect on whether these themes are how you want to be living, or if you might like to set intentions to live by different ones. For example, if you notice that your themes are 'exhausted, stressed, frustrated, or any other themes that are not healthy for you and might be keeping you stuck, think about the values and themes you would like to be living by and set them as a goal. Then whenever you find yourself making decisions about how you spend your time, or are planning your day, ask yourself if the decisions you are making will enable you to be in alignment with the values that you have set.

As a creative person, my mind sometimes has difficulty focussing (as so many ideas are flying around in there!) so I find this task quite challenging but it is so rewarding. Whenever I am feeling overwhelmed or overloaded, I come back to my three words and see if I am still in alignment with these core values.

The three words I set as an intention to live by this year were:

Creativity: Compassion: Connection

I keep them on a vision board in my office, on my phone as a daily reminder (you can set it in your calendar to pop up whenever you like), and I use them to guide me in choices about how I spend my time and approach my work.

Burn-Brighter Step:

- Tell the story of the past week, and list 'the good, the bad and the ugly bits'. Keep asking yourself 'and anything else?' until you have created your story.
- Once you have your lists, think about what themes they might represent, and reflect how you feel about them.
- Now think about the themes and values you would like to be living by to create your story for the next week – write them down and pick just three to start focussing on.
- At the end of the week, reflect on what changes you noticed in how you feel and how you showed up at work and at home.

Forgive, not forget.

"Thinking is difficult, that's why most people judge."
—Carl Jung

Combined with acceptance and reflection, forgiveness is a powerful and essential tool in your resilience toolkit as it can release you from the burden of carrying guilt, shame, anger, and a whole host of emotional responses to a past event that are causing you more harm every time you revisit it.

The Collins English dictionary defines forgiveness as:

"To stop blaming or being angry with someone for something that person has done, or not punish them for something" (Szasz)

This can include yourself too!

Embracing your past mistakes or decisions and accepting that they were the best you could do with the resources, support and knowledge you had at that time is no easy task, as it involves confronting those things about yourself that irritate or displease you. Very often we are far more critical of ourselves than we are of other people. Can you be your own compassionate friend and forgive yourself too?

It may seem counterintuitive, but holding onto anger and resentment about other people's actions and behaviours actually harms you way more than it harms them—and it harms you more and more each time you fire up those anger circuits in your mind.

As the Buddhist concept of the 'second dart' goes – we all will suffer some physical or mental discomfort at some point in our lives – but our response (the second dart) can often be more damaging than the first 'dart' ever was. This is because your brain (as we learned in Chapter 2) doesn't distinguish between each retelling – your brain thinks it's actually happening, so it pumps you full of the stress response cocktail of hormones and neurotransmitters.

As these chemicals flood your mind and body, they prime you for fight or flight. If these are not processed and released they keep you trapped in a fight, flight, freeze, or fawn state and contribute to you burning out.

So, to be resilient, we need to recognise these responses and find healthier ways of responding that don't cause us further harm.

Now I want to be very clear here, this is not about declaring the actions of those that upset or hurt us as OK! Forgiving someone, including yourself, is really about allowing yourself the freedom to accept that the behaviour has happened, to reflect on it (as we have learned in the previous two sections of this chapter) and to work out a way of processing your feelings using your higher logical thinking and creative brain. This is much easier when you are not clouded by the stressed-out, emotional brain flooding your body with cortisol. This affirmation from the late Louise Hay is also a useful prompt to remember;

'What good can come of this situation?'

That may seem like a strange question to ask when thinking about forgiving something that has hurt us in some way, but it is often when things go wrong, or when we are faced with disappointment, rejection, or loss of some form that we make decisions or take actions that can change our life in a positive way. So, by looking for what we can learn about ourselves and others from situations that are hurtful to us, we can actually benefit and grow from the experience. It is pointless to hold onto anger, resentment and other energy-sapping emotions as we are the only ones who suffer from the effects of those emotional responses and not the original perpetrator.

I hope that by the end of this book you will have moved away from blaming yourself for feeling burned out to understanding why it is not your fault. Hopefully, you are learning to love and forgive yourself for feeling that way. As Carl Jung also said,

"The most terrifying thing is to accept oneself completely."

Burn-Brighter step:

- What is one small step that you could take right now to start forgiving yourself or others for something that has happened in the past?
- How could that make a difference to you and to how you respond to them in future?
- How could forgiveness affect your energy levels each day?

Mindset really matters.

"I am not what happened to me,
I am what I choose to become."

—Carl Jung

This is the controversial bit, so get prepared to be challenged by the next few pages!

As a parent to two teens, I have had so many 'heated debates' about this issue when challenging thoughts and beliefs shared around the family dinner table. *'Oh, you are not going into that mindset stuff again, Mum – I know what I believe and you can't change my mind!'*

Sound familiar? Well to a certain extent, I think we all get caught in this pattern of thinking. However, it is my hope that this book will help us begin to break free of the confines of old, fixed mindsets. The truth is, our old thoughts and beliefs can be changed or even eliminated from our minds.

As we learned in Chapter 2, our brains are complicated and amazing, but in the simplest of terms, our thoughts and beliefs are just chemical processes. They are just the electrical stimulation of a bunch of neurons wired together in patterns we have formed based on previous experiences, much of which was created before the age of seven.

Scientists now recognise that, with the right tools and practice, these connections (even deep-rooted ones) can be unconnected and rewired, amplified, or tuned down into whatever new arrangements we choose them to be in.

Remember Hebb's law, paraphrased by journalist Carla Schatz as "***Nerves that fire together wire together***" (**Shatz**) that we considered in Chapter 2? By working on our mindset, we can train and rewire our brain into believing, thinking, and feeling whatever we choose to!

Some of the tools described in the rest of this chapter can all help with this, but before we get to those, let's take a look at growth mindsets versus fixed mindsets and see how they can contribute to and help you break out of the burnout cycle.

Growth vs. Fixed Mindsets

Psychologist Carol Dweck has written extensively on this subject. In her groundbreaking book *Mindset* she explains this concept in this simple way:

> ***How you view yourself can determine everything .***

With a ***fixed mindset***, you believe that your intelligence, ability to learn or beliefs are unchangeable.

Your mind will want to prove yourself correct over and over rather than learning from your mistakes.

With a ***growth mindset*** however, when we fail or get let down, we understand that while it may be a painful experience for a short time, crucially, *it does not become who we are.*

We can assign a different meaning to our past experiences, thoughts, and beliefs and are *not* defined by them.

Instead of allowing the failure to reflect on or define us, those with a growth mindset allow the experience to be a learning opportunity. They accept that it can be worked through

162

with the right support, gentle curiosity, and most importantly, self-compassion.

We can always learn from our mistakes or failures. The legendary basketball coach John Wooden said,

'You're not a failure until you start to assign blame. That's when you stop learning from your mistakes – you deny them.'

This is why I started this section on acceptance – there is a method to this process!

I love this quote from the great Sir Ken Robinson who was a thought leader in the field of education and creativity: *"If you're not prepared to be wrong, you'll never come up with anything original."*

In *Mindset: The New Psychology of Success*, Dweck writes:

I've seen so many people with this one consuming goal of proving themselves—in the classroom, in their careers, and in their relationships. Every situation calls for a confirmation of their intelligence, personality, or character. Every situation is evaluated: Will I succeed or fail? Will I look smart or dumb? Will I be accepted or rejected? Will I feel like a winner or a loser?

There's another mindset in which these traits are not simply a hand you're dealt and have to live with, always trying to convince yourself and others that you have a royal flush when you're secretly worried it's a pair of tens. In this mindset, the hand you're dealt is just the starting point for development. This growth mindset is based on the belief that your basic qualities are things you can cultivate through your efforts.

In other words, a fixed mindset could be seen as a real contributor to burnout as you will be constantly judging yourself as an inherent success or failure, according to whatever measures of 'success' you are setting for yourself and you see yourself as either a winner or loser, not as someone who can improve or change.

With a growth mindset, however, you are able to allow some self-compassion in considering how you perform at work, and are not automatically criticising or judging yourself every day.

This fundamental difference in how you respond to everyday situations changes your entire physiology. Suddenly, you are sending a whole different bunch of neurotransmitters and hormones around your body, which will have a significant impact on how you feel both physically and mentally.

Is it that simple?

Really?

Just change your mindset and you can never burn out again?

Well, in some ways, yes! But in reality, this is just one tool that can work really well with all the other tools I'm sharing in this book. Using them in a combination that is right for you will empower you to break free from the burnout cycle and be much more resilient to whatever challenges head your way.

Mindset is crucial in helping you break free of burnout because, I'm sorry to say, you *will* fail in this process.

It is not any judgement on you or your abilities to hit goals (remember that goal trauma is probably the reason you got trapped in the burnout cycle!), but it is just a fact of life.

In any change process, relapse is an integral part, so to be able to make any lasting changes to how you work and live, it is really important to have a growth mindset so you are prepared for the times you find yourself slipping back into the old patterns of burnout-causing behaviour.

When this happens, you need to be able to go back through the steps outlined earlier in this chapter:

Acceptance, Reflection, Forgiveness, Growth.

And, especially important, remember that you are not defined by failure. In applying a growth mindset, you need to be curious, compassionate, and honest with yourself so you can understand all the reasons why you lapsed. Then, you can adjust the tools and support you are applying to help you get back on track with your recovery.

Once you have done this, you may be feeling strong enough to tackle some other ways you can challenge the workplace stressors that you have been experiencing by exploring the organisational and legal protections in your place of work.

Let's get Physical.

"Take care of your body. it's the only place you have to live in."

—Jim Rohn

I have to admit here, I'm no gym bunny or runner, but I know lots of people who have the discipline and who enjoy getting out for a run every day. It has been described as a form of meditation as the feet pound their rhythm on the ground and the mind is focussed on taking one step after another. This gives plenty of time for Acceptance and Forgiveness. Although I say I'm not a runner, I have completed two marathons for charity and did find the training and preparation for them all encompassing. I couldn't think about anything else for months! Once on the road, it is very difficult to channel any energy into anything else. You are directing all your focus on coordination and stamina to get you through the session.

It is important to be mindful, however, that exercising to compete or achieve a specific weight or fitness goal *could* be counterproductive and contribute to burnout, *if* you allow it to be another thing to beat yourself up about if you don't hit the standards you set. As this is a book about helping you to break free from burnout, I'm interested in physical exercise that sustains you and doesn't turn into another goal to achieve.

As outlined in Chapter 2, physical activity can help you to process the chemical tsunami that is released when you are perceiving a threat or have been triggered to respond as if you are under threat. Neurotransmitters and hormones flood your body and unless they get processed or released, they can build up and cause an inflammatory response or be converted to other harmful products that get stored in your body.

If you have ever watched a wildlife documentary and saw an antelope being chased by a predator and escaping – you may have witnessed it standing and shaking, trembling and jumping about afterwards. This is the physical release of the adrenaline and cortisol that has just primed that animal to flee the predator, diverting blood and oxygen supplies to the muscles and increasing its heart rate to run as fast as it can to get away.

Once it has shaken off this cocktail of flight stimulators, it goes back to the herd and continues with its day. Imagine if we humans could 'shake it off' every time we were triggered? That would make an awesome documentary!

My daughter was experiencing challenges at school (as well as coping with adolescence and all that brings to our body and mind) and she asked me to buy her a punchbag to help her process her anger and frustration. This was her releasing those stress hormones using exercise, and it really helped her to calm down whenever she felt like things were getting too much or she had a bad day at school.

Exercise can be fun (yes, really!) especially if it is a social occasion such as joining a class, or being part of a club or team. It could also help you be active more regularly if you have the accountability of having to show up for a class or team training session. Even going out for a walk with friends or family could really make a difference to your recovery, especially if you get outside and have the widely evidenced benefits of connecting with Nature too. I recently joined a women's kickboxing class and have really noticed how much better I feel after an hour of working out and connecting with my fellow classmates, even when we are swinging punches at each other!

Burn-Brighter Step:

- Think about how active you are each day, week, month?
- What activities do you enjoy?
- What could you try more of?

Commitment step: go to your journal and complete a commitment pledge to increase physical activity, even if it is for just five minutes a day.

Have a Spiritual Awakening

Meanings are not determined by situations. We determine
ourselves by the meanings we ascribe to situations.
—Alfred Adler

I have to confess (no pun intended!), I do not follow any religion, but have found my own spiritual practice through mediation and creativity.

Having a faith or spiritual practice could help you become more resilient. The teachings and social connection that faith communities offer can give you a different perspective on the stress factors that are causing you to burn out and also the bigger picture of where your work fits into your life. It can also have a bearing on how you identify – i.e. if you are a follower of a faith or spiritual practice, your identity is not defined solely by your job or your place in the organisation that you work for, but is also influenced by the teachings of whatever faith you are following. This means while you could be exposed to the same stressors as fellow colleagues, you may ascribe completely different meanings that dictate how you respond depending on how you view yourself and your place in the world.

You may also have a community within your practice that you can discuss whatever is causing you to feel stressed and find ways of dealing with it that align with your spiritual values.

On the flip side, the doctrines that some spiritual practices teach may have caused you to form beliefs about yourself and your place in society that could be contributing to your burning out. It's important to balance the connection and comfort that a spiritual practice can bring with the interpretations of religious texts that you may have been taught from an early age. Allow yourself to question those interpretations as an adult and how they may be influencing you and your ability to form healthy boundaries on your time and energy. This is often something people are afraid to do as questioning belief can be seen as against the rules, but, there are many things that we assign meaning to as our younger selves that can be seen in different ways as our adult selves. We need to give ourselves permission to reflect on them.

Have you ever gone back to the original texts of your spiritual practice and really thought about what they are teaching you? This sounds like a deep thing to do, especially when you are probably feeling exhausted and overwhelmed, but could be something that changes how you look at your practice. Really think about what it means to you, through your own lens and not from someone else's interpretation.

This type of reflection is a form of meditation, as you allow yourself to look in a different way at something you may have been taught about for most of your life but may have never really thought about. Remember what we learned about meditation in Chapter 9? It can change your brain structure and even cause parts of it to grow, as well as help you to process and release stress from the mind and body, so it's a win-win for anyone working through burnout recovery.

Some religions and spiritual practices use repeated mantras or affirmations and that's what we'll be looking at next.

Affirmations and Celebrations

Earlier in the book, we learned about Hebbs law that explains how our brains can rewire themselves if you repeatedly stimulate neurons next to each other. So if you repeat thoughts often enough, it can form new neural networks and hardwire into your brain.

Affirmations are a self-help/development practice that involves repeating a positive statement regularly to induce a supportive belief or overcome barriers or blocks to achieving goals. It is important to remember that your subconscious mind won't fall for something it inherently doesn't believe, so 'toxic positivity' won't benefit you here. The magic happens if you can manage to craft statements that acknowledge the difficulties that you are working to overcome, and include the tools described throughout this chapter (acceptance, reflection, forgiveness and growth). Affirmations incorporating these can have remarkable results in a short space of time!

If you combine regular repetition of the affirmation, with actions that acknowledge or support the direction your affirmation is taking you, you can overcome the fear of moving out of your comfort zone and really implement the 'growth mindset' we learned about earlier in this chapter.

This can really boost the 'happy hormones' by recognising your successes and every small step you take to move away from the situation or beliefs you are trying to let go of.

As we learned in Chapter 2, our brains are naturally wired to focus on the negatives, on what went wrong or what we fail at, as this is what our primitive safety system uses to keep us safe from getting hurt. By boosting the neural networks with thoughts of success and positive messages, we can redress the balance and ensure a regular supply of positive mood enhancing goodies pulsing through our minds. This will boost our energy and enable us to feel less stressed and more resilient and confident in our ability to deal with life's challenges each day.

By saying your affirmations out loud, or even in a mirror, you can enhance their effectiveness. As bestselling author Mel Robbins explains in her brilliant book *The High Five Habit,* - giving yourself a 'high five' every day in the mirror as you repeat your affirmations can rewire your brain for acceptance, self-forgiveness, and success.

Here are some examples of affirmations you could try saying out loud to yourself:

- By reading this book on beating burnout I am taking steps to reclaim my life, my energy, and my boundaries.
- I trust that I can build a more resilient, joyful, and happier self.
- Whatever happened in the past is history, I am learning to accept where I am right now and love the person I have become.
- I am the author of my life, and every day I start a new story. Today I choose love, acceptance, and growth.

Burn-Brighter Step:

- What affirmations could you start using to help you build resilience and break free from burnout? Write a list of ten phrases you could use.
- Now choose one to repeat every day in the mirror for a week. Take note of how you feel over time.
- To remind yourself of the affirmation, you could add it as a calendar entry or screensaver, or record yourself saying it and listen in the morning and evening.

Do an Energy Audit

A final tool to share is a personal energy audit, although it could be used right at the start of the process of your recovery journey as it can help you to identify where you might need to make changes to protect your time and energy. Essentially it enables you to identify which areas of your life are energising and which are stressful or tiring and causing you to use energy and add to your fatigue. This is also available as a FREE PDF download available here.

Your Personal Energy Audit
What areas of your life give you energy and what saps it?
- Imagine you start each day with an 'energy account' credited with £100.
- For each activity, thought, or experience that makes you feel energised you gain £1,
- For each that makes you stressed, anxious, angry, or saps energy, you lose £1.
- How much will your 'energy account' have at the end of a typical working day?
- Will you be in credit or overdrawn?

Think about your own experiences in the following areas:

Physical actions: Everyday tasks such as diet, exercise, general housework, commuting.
- Do you have any relaxation activities?

- Do you sleep well? This can vary for individuals but six to eight hours a day is considered healthy. Remember it is during sleep that your body and brain repair themself and you process thoughts and experiences in your mind.
- Do you eat well? Having foods that meet all of your nutrient requirements and release energy steadily through the day instead of quick-release sugary foods that can cause your energy to crash.
- Do you exercise regularly?

Or Emotional events: Looking after yourself and others.
- Do you feel appreciated by your work or family? Remember Maslow's hierarchy of needs and the attachment theory we talked about in Chapter 7.
- Are you under pressure to perform at work?
- Are you dealing with change?
- Are you caring for dependents or someone who is emotionally demanding?

Mental factors: Is your mind stimulated or overloaded?
- Do you have inspiring people to talk to? Or are they 'energy vampires' who suck the life and soul out of social situations with their emotional needs or behaviours? These are people who take more energy from you instead of sharing the energy or giving some back. For example, do you have someone in your life who makes you feel tired, unsupported,

depleted, and maybe even a little sad after you spend time with them?

- Do you have happy or conflicting relationships at home or at work?
- Is your life predictable, or does it feel out of control?
- Do you worry about past or future events to the extent that these worries predominate your thinking and affect decision making at work?
- Do you have an endless 'to do' list? Feel like you never finish anything?
- Do you recognise the stuff you do finish?

Inspiration: Do you have a sense of purpose or inspiration in your life?

- Do you have a supportive person who has your back and encourages you to grow?
- Do you have free 'slow thinking' time to create headspace, or are you constantly on edge?
- Do you use stimulants/alcohol or drugs to help you get through challenging times?
- Do you have a community or other shared connection outside of your work and family life?

Remember, when thinking about these questions, it is important to not judge yourself or compare yourself to anyone else. These are merely meant as prompts to let you examine where you spend your time and energy and reflect on how the activities affect your own energy levels. Please use your journal or the table provided here to start counting your energy account inputs and withdrawals.

Personal Energy Audit – list your energy drains (-) and energy gains (+)							
Physical		Emotional		Mental		Inspirational	
Everyday activities (e.g., work, Diet, relaxation, exercise.		Personal and relationship issues, e.g. as self-criticism, judging yourself or others, dependants.		e.g. Work interests, hobbies, repetitive tasks, control over activities		e.g. Mentors, teachers, connection, goals, motivation.	
Activity/ Issue	+/-	Activity/ Issue	+/-	Activity/ Issue	+/-	Activity/ Issue	+/-
Total Drains (-)		Total Drains (-)		Total Drains (-)		Total Drains (-)	
Total Gains (+)		Total Gains (+)		Total Gains (+)		Total Gains (+)	

Look at the total gains (+) and the total drains (-) Are they balanced? Are you overdrawn?

What steps can you take to tip the balance more in favour of the gains to boost your energy account?

Write down three actions you can take here:

1.	2.	3.

Congratulations! You have now started to take back control of your own energy. You can use this tool to check in and keep on top of the 'drainers and gainers' whenever you feel your energy levels sapping.

If you have found this worksheet useful and want to find out how our Power Hour or Self-Care for the Exhausted coaching could help you beat burnout and become more resilient, please visit our website www.worksafeandwell.co.uk for more information.

Chapter 11
End Thoughts

Thanks for reading this book. I hope that the steps and tools shared here will help you like they helped me and that your life will become less stressed and more joyful as you build your own resilience toolkit and break free from burnout for good.

I also hope that you can start writing on your own walls and building new beliefs about what makes you happy, belong, and feel connected to the people and things that matter most to you.

It has taken me many years of suffering through fear, guilt, and shame to be able to share my experiences and pull together the tools detailed in this book. It is my ambition that every workplace becomes a place that does not harm their workers mental or physical health.

The first step in that process is calling out burnout for what it really is: exposure to unmanaged work-related stress, so the tables can be turned and we can all take responsibility for dealing with it, both in how work is organised, and in how we recognise and respond to stress triggers.

It has taken over a decade for me to learn how to do this, and I am happy to report that all the work I now choose to do brings me joy, and allows me to make an impact on many more people by helping them to live happier healthier lives too.

Please share this book with someone you think might benefit from some support. Let's build a movement to call out burnout and be more compassionate towards ourselves and our fellow workers so we can all burn brighter.

I am grateful for you, dear reader, for taking the time to consider my musings here, and hope that it will help you to make some positive changes in your life.

You are enough.

You deserve to be happy.

You can control how you feel, no matter what life throws at you.

Now, go and build your resilience toolkit! Let's make burnout a distant memory in your life. And remember:

"It is not enough to be compassionate; we must act."
Dalai Lama

Acknowledgments

I wouldn't be writing this book if it wasn't for my beautiful family who have supported me throughout the early mornings and late nights, through the highs and the lows. For the past 31 years since I met my amazing creative, caring husband, John, he has inspired me every day.

We have done so much together; thanks for listening and backing me 100 percent.

Thanks also to Dad and Dot – you have been my rocks, my mentors and my sanctuary, getting me through some really tough times. I can never express how grateful I am for everything you have done for me and my family.

There are so many more stars that light up my life and have guided me, inspired me, and helped me learn how to find myself from the shell I was hiding in and taught me to live, love and laugh again. If I started naming some of them I would feel so bad about the ones I had left out! You know who you are and I am truly grateful to have you in my life. It would probably double the length of this book if I were to thank everyone who has supported me to get to the point where I was ready and able to write this book. So, if you have been part of my inner circle, or shared time with me over the past 51 years, please know that you have left an imprint on my heart in some way, and I thank you for it, whether that was a positive or not so positive experience.

To the teachers, tutors, musicians, writers, and artists who have guided me to a path of mindfulness and creativity – I salute you and thank you for your generosity in sharing your knowledge and talents with the world.

And finally, I have to mention my SPS coach Kerk Murray and editors at Wandering Words media and all the Self-Publishing School and launch team for supporting me to get this book birthed and out into the world.

I am truly grateful.

Thank you.

WANT MORE?

Listen to the Creating Resilience Podcast

Available on all major platforms or start here:
https://anchor.fm/ann-diment-changemaker

AUTHOR BIO

Ann Diment is a 'Creative Changemaker,' helping clients find better balance to beat burnout using the creative arts and other holistic ways to support wellbeing. She has worked tirelessly across multiple sectors, promoting health and wellbeing issues for all of her professional life.

Ann passionately shares how to take a more creative and human-centred approach to supporting wellbeing, drawing from her lived experience of recovery from PTSD and depression.

Teaching self-compassion, creativity, and empathy as wellbeing tools, her mission is to help build more resilient and engaged communities and smash the stigma around talking about mental health by empowering everyone to start 'what matters to me' conversations in work, education, and social settings.

She is an accredited advanced EFT practitioner, offering transformational group and personal coaching, with over 20 years' experience in managing workplace well-being, Health and Safety. Ann holds a Chartered Fellowship of IOSH, is a Personalised Care Institute accredited trainer and ambassador, and judges an international H&S award.

To keep her (and her family) sane, she nurtures a socially engaged creative practice as a published poet and professional artist and performer with her life partner and their band. She is also a mum of two beautiful souls who are her greatest teachers every day.

Love this book?

Don't forget to leave a review!
Every review matters, so we can reach more people who need
to break free from burnout.
Please head over to wherever you purchased this book to
leave a review so I can learn and grow as an author and share
more ways to smash stigma with the world.
Every book purchased is supporting my chosen charity
PTSD UK
On behalf of them and myself, I thank you from the bottom
of my heart.

BIBLIOGRAPHY

- Arts Council England. 2022. "Creative Health & Wellbeing." https://www.artscouncil.org.uk/creative-health-wellbeing.
- Association for Play Therapy (APT). n.d. "Association for Play Therapy (APT)." https://www.a4pt.org/.
- Blackburn with Darwen Borough Council. n.d. "Childhood Trauma." https://www.blackburn.gov.uk/health/childhood-trauma.
- Bowlby, John. "Attachment and Loss: Attachment." United Kingdom: Basic Books, 1969.
- Brown, S., et al. n.d. "The Warwick-Edinburgh Mental Wellbeing Scale (WEMWBS)." University of Warwick. https://warwick.ac.uk/fac/sci/med/research/platform/wemwbs/.
- Burkeman, Oliver. "Oliver Burkeman's last column: the eight secrets to a (fairly) fulfilled life." The Guardian, September 4, 2020. https://www.theguardian.com/lifeandstyle/2020/sep/04/oliver-burkemans-last-column-the-eight-secrets-to-a-fairly-fulfilled-life.
- Centers for Disease Control and Prevention (CDC). n.d. "Adverse Childhood Experiences (ACEs)." https://www.cdc.gov/violenceprevention/aces/index.html.
- Church, Dawson, et al. "Clinical EFT as an evidence-based practice for the treatment of psychological and physiological conditions: A systematic review." Frontiers in Psychology, 2022. 13: 951451. https://doi.org/10.3389/fpsyg.2022.951451.
- Dearing, Lucy. "The missing lonely: exploring direct and indirect measures of loneliness." The Health Foundation, Decem-

ber 18, 2019. https://www.health.org.uk/news-and-comment/
charts-and-infographics/the-missing-lonely.

- Diamond, Marian. "Older Brains, New Connections." Davidson
Films, Inc. YouTube, July 14, 2010. https://www.youtube.com/
watch?v=0APJD-wN7MA.

- Diamond, Marian C., et al. "The effects of an enriched environment on the histology of the rat cerebral cortex." Journal of Compar-
ative Neurology, 1964. 123 (1): 111-119. https://doi.org/10.1002/
cne.901230110.

- D'souza, Paul J., et al. "Relaxation training and written emotional
disclosure for tension or migraine headaches: a randomised,
controlled trial." Annals of Behavioral Medicine, 2008. 36 (1):
21-32. https://www.ncbi.nlm.nih.gov/pmc/articles/PMC2931412/.

- Dweck, Carol S. "Mindset." Robinson, 2012.

- Dweck, Carol S. "Mindset: The New Psychology of Success."
Random House Publishing Group, 2007.

- Feldt, Taru, et al. "The 9-item Bergen Burnout Inventory: Facto-
rial validity across organisations and measurements of longitudinal
data." Industrial Health, 2014. 52 (2): 102-112. PubMed. https://
pubmed.ncbi.nlm.nih.gov/24366535/.

- Felitti, Vincent J., et al. "Relationship of Childhood Abuse
and Household Dysfunction to Many of the Leading Causes of
Death in Adults." American Journal of Preventive Medicine, vol.
14, no. 4, 1998, pp. 245-258, https://doi.org/10.1016/S0749-
3797(98)00017-8.

- Golden, Bernard. "How Adverse Childhood Experiences (ACEs)
Impact Adult Anger." Psychology Today, June 6, 2021,
https://www.psychologytoday.com/us/blog/overcoming-self-sab-

otage/202106/how-adverse-childhood-experiences-aces-im-pact-adult-anger.

- Golden, Bernard. "How Maladaptive Perfectionism Can Arouse Anger." Psychology Today, December 31, 2020, https://www.psychologytoday.com/us/blog/overcoming-self-sabotage/202012/how-maladaptive-perfectionism-can-arouse-anger.

- Goleman, Daniel. "Emotional Intelligence: Why It Can Matter More Than IQ." Random House Publishing Group, 2005.

- Goleman, Daniel, and Matthew Wheeland. "Hot to Help | Greater Good." Greater Good Science Center, March 1, 2008, https://greatergood.berkeley.edu/article/item/hot_to_help.

- Greater Good Science Center. "Empathy Definition | What Is Empathy?" https://greatergood.berkeley.edu/topic/empathy/definition.

- Health and Safety Executive (HSE). "Health and Safety at Work etc Act 1974 - legislation explained." https://www.hse.gov.uk/legislation/hswa.htm.

- Health and Safety Executive (HSE). "Work-related stress: A guide." https://www.hse.gov.uk/stress/assets/docs/eurostress.pdf.

- Hebb, Donald O. "The organization of behaviour; a neuropsychological theory." Wiley, 1949. https://psycnet.apa.org/record/1950-02200-000.

- Howick, Jeremy, et al. "Establishing a causal link between social relationships and health using the Bradford Hill Guidelines." SSM - Population Health, vol. 9, 2019, p. 100402, https://www.sciencedirect.com/science/article/pii/S2352827318303501.

- International Standards Organisation. "ISO 45003:2021 - Occupational health and safety management — Psychological health and safety at work — Guidelines for managing psychosocial risks." https://www.iso.org/standard/64283.html.

- Jones, Lora, and Dearbail Jordan. "Bumble closes to give 'burnt-out' staff a week's break." BBC News, June 22, 2021. https://www.bbc.co.uk/news/business-57562230.

- King, Vanessa. "10 Keys to Happier Living." Headline, 2017.

- Lewis, Rachel, et al. "Developing an understanding of moral injury in business settings." Affinity Health at Work, May 2022, https://www.affinityhealthatwork.com/our-research/1214.

- Litz, B. T., et al. "Moral injury and moral repair in war veterans: a preliminary model and intervention strategy." Clinical Psychology Review, 2009. Vol. 29, no. 8, pp. 695-706. PMID: 19683376.

- Lowey, Helen. "National household survey of adverse childhood experiences and their relationship with resilience to health-harming behaviours in England." PubMed, May 2, 2014.

- Marmot, Michael. "Fair society, healthy lives: the Marmot Review: strategic review of health inequalities in England post-2010." GOV. UK, January 1, 2010.

- Maslach, Christina, Susan E. Jackson, et al. "Job Burnout." Annual Review of Psychology, January 17, 2019.

- Maslach, Christina, et al. "Maslach burnout inventory." Scarecrow Education, 1997.

- Maslach, Christina, and Susan E. Jackson. "The measurement of experienced burnout." Journal of Organizational Behaviour, 1981. Vol. 2, pp. 99-113.

- Maslow, Abraham. "Motivation and Personality." Harper & Brothers, 1954.

- Meaney, Michael J., et al. "Effect of Neonatal Handling on Age-Related Impairments Associated with the Hippocampus." Science, 1988. Vol. 239, no. 4841, pp. 766-768.

- Merriam-Webster Dictionary. "Empathy Definition & Meaning." https://www.merriam-webster.com/dictionary/empathy.

- Merriam-Webster Dictionary. "Stress Definition & Meaning." https://www.merriam-webster.com/dictionary/stress.

- Moiseff, Andrew, and Jonathan Copeland. "Firefly Synchrony: A Behavioral Strategy to Minimize Visual Clutter." Science, 2010. Vol. 329, no. 5988, pp. 181-184.

- National Institute for Clinical Excellence (NICE). "Overview | Mental wellbeing at work | Guidance." March 2, 2022. https://www.nice.org.uk/guidance/gid-phg98/overview.

- National Institute for Clinical Excellence NICE. "Recommendations | Mental Wellbeing at Work |Guidance." NICE. March 2, 2022. https://www.nice.org.uk/guidance/ng10087.

- Occupational Safety and Health Administration (OSHA). "Employer Responsibilities." https://www.osha.gov/workers/employer-responsibilities.

- Öngür, D., and J. L. Price. "The organization of networks within the orbital and medial prefrontal cortex of rats, monkeys and humans." Cerebral Cortex, 2000. Vol. 10, no. 3, pp. 206-219.

- PTSD UK. "Hypervigilance and PTSD – PTSD UK." https://www.ptsduk.org/hypervigilance-and-ptsd/.

- Raichle, Marcus E. "The brain's default mode network." Annual Review of Neuroscience, 2015. Vol. 38, no. 8, pp. 433-447.

- Robbins, Mel. "The High 5 Habit." Accessed November 1, 2022. https://www.high5habit.com/.

- Salovey, Peter, and John D. Mayer. "Emotional Intelligence. Imagination." Cognition and Personality 9, no. 3 (1990): 185–211.
- Saner, Emine. "A Career Change Saved My Life: The People Who Built Better Lives after Burnout." The Guardian. June 8, 2021. https://www.theguardian.com/society/2021/jun/08/a-career-change-saved-my-life-the-people-who-built-better-lives-after-burnout.
- Scaer, Robert C. "The Body Bears the Burden: Trauma, Dissociation, and Disease." Routledge, 2014.
- Schnall, S., J. Harber, T. Stefanucci, and L. Proffitt. "Social Support and the Perception of Geographical Slant." Journal of Experimental Social Psychology 44, no. 5 (2008): 1246-1255. https://doi.org/10.1016/j.jesp.2008.04.004.
- Shatz, Carla J. "The Developing Brain." Scientific American, n.d.
- Shay, Jonathan. "Achilles in Vietnam: Combat Trauma and the Undoing of Character." Scribner, 1995.
- Shay, Jonathan. "Moral Injury." Psychoanalytic Psychology 31, no. 2 (2014): 182–191. https://doi.org/10.1037/a0035667.
- Shay, Jonathan. "Odysseus in America: Combat Trauma and the Trials of Homecoming." Scribner, 2003.
- Stapleton, Peta. "Is Therapy Facing a Revolution?" TEDxRobina. YouTube. December 7, 2018. https://www.youtube.com/watch?v=0Vu0Tibt1bQ&feature=youtu.be.
- Stapleton, Peta. "Science of Tapping." Dr Peta Stapleton, 2022. https://www.petastapleton.com/science-of-tapping-2022/.
- Szasz, Thomas. "Forgiveness Definition and Meaning." Collins English Dictionary. Collins Dictionary, n.d. https://www.collinsdictionary.com/dictionary/english/forgiveness.

- Tage, S., et al. "The Copenhagen Burnout Inventory: A new tool for the assessment of burnout." Work & Stress 19, no. 3 (2005): 192-207. https://www.tandfonline.com/doi/abs/10.1080/02678370500297720.

- Tang, Yi Yuan, et al. "Meditation improves self-regulation over the life span." Annals of the New York Academy of Sciences 1307, no. 1 (2014): 104-111.

- Tenaglia, Simona. "Workplace Wellbeing Questionnaire: Methodology." What Works Wellbeing. https://whatworkswellbeing.org/resources/workplace-wellbeing-questionnaire-methodology/.

- Turnbull, Gordon. "Trauma: From Lockerbie to 7/7: How Trauma Affects Our Minds and How We Fight Back." Transworld Publishers Limited, 2012.

- Valtorta, N. K., et al. "Loneliness and social isolation as risk factors for coronary heart disease and stroke: systematic review and meta-analysis of longitudinal observational studies." Heart 102 (2016): 1009-1016.

- Van der Kolk, Bessel A. "The Body Keeps the Score: Brain, Mind, and Body in the Healing of Trauma." Penguin Publishing Group, 2015.

- Van Tulleken, Alexander, and Helen Chatterjee. "Does Art Heal? What is the Evidence? What should the Policy be?" YouTube, March 24, 2021. https://www.youtube.com/watch?v=zWQ1bYEwpCs&t=5692s.

- Williamson, Victoria, et al. "Occupational moral injury and mental health: Systematic review and meta-analysis." The British Journal of Psychiatry 212, no. 6 (2018): 339-346.

- World Health Organization (WHO). "Burn-out an 'occupational phenomenon': International Classification of Diseases." May 28, 2019, https://www.who.int/news/item/28-05-2019-burn-out-an-occupational-phenomenon-international-classification-of-diseases.

- World Health Organization (WHO). "Long working hours increasing deaths from heart disease and stroke: WHO, ILO." May 17, 2021. https://www.who.int/news/item/17-05-2021-long-working-hours-increasing-deaths-from-heart-disease-and-stroke-who-ilo.

- World Health Organization (WHO). "Social Isolation and Loneliness - Social Isolation and Loneliness." WHO, July 29, 2021. https://www.who.int/news-room/questions-and-answers/item/social-isolation-and-loneliness

- Zinn, Jon Kabat, et al. "The Mindful Way through Depression". The Guilford Press, 2007.

selfpublishing.com

NOW IT'S YOUR TURN

Discover the EXACT 3-step blueprint you need to become a bestselling author in as little as 3 months.

Self-Publishing School helped me, and now I want them to help you with this FREE resource to begin outlining your book!

Even if you're busy, bad at writing, or don't know where to start, you CAN write a bestseller and build your best life.

With tools and experience across a variety of niches and professions, Self-Publishing School is the only resource you need to take your book to the finish line!

DON'T WAIT

Say "YES" to becoming a bestseller:

https://selfpublishing.com/friend/

Follow the steps on the page to get a FREE resource to get started on your book and unlock a discount to get started with SelfPublishing.com

Printed in Great Britain
by Amazon

38547767R00116